PRAISE FOR

Front Office Success
How to Satisfy Patients and Boost the Bottom Line

༄

"This book is now essential reading for all my front office staff. Elizabeth Woodcock is the expert on running an efficient medical practice, and the practical wisdom and insights she shares in *Front Office Success* are what every front office employee needs to reach peak performance. She gets right to the point in a clear, straightforward text that should be on the bookshelf of every medical practice."

KEVIN COLTON, MD
Pediatrician
CHILDREN'S MEDICAL GROUP, ATLANTA

༄

"Properly applied, Elizabeth Woodcock's newest book, *Front Office Success*, is sure to propel medical practice staff to a higher level of performance and become a well-used handbook for all front office employees. Woodcock does an amazing job listing out and explaining real-world actions (as well as) provides tools for both newly hired and seasoned staff. Many of the solutions that Woodcock explores can be applied throughout the medical practice — from the front to the back office. I would highly recommend *Front Office Success* to all colleagues looking to set themselves apart in this highly competitive market!"

CINDERELLA TOLLEFSEN, CPC, FACMPE
Practice Manager
HILLSIDE FAMILY MEDICINE, ANCHORAGE

༄

More praise . . .

"Elizabeth Woodcock's *Front Office Success*, her latest book on the operations and management of the physician's office, is a 'must-have'.... The book covers all the bases – and basics – of front desk operations.... Woodcock knows her audience and writes well for it. The book is clear, concise, and easy to read. Designed as a training manual and teaching tool, it has tips, lists, do's and don'ts, examples, self-tests, and a quiz for each chapter. The book is a self-help learning tool for both the beginner and the seasoned. In short, for anyone managing a front desk staff, hiring office staff, or training personnel, *Front Office Success* is a timely and welcome addition to our tool kit for improving the day-to-day functioning of the physician's office."

GERRY GOODRICH, JD, MPH
Director, Practice Operations
WEILL CORNELL PHYSICIAN ORGANIZATION, WEILL CORNELL MEDICAL COLLEGE, NEW YORK

Front Office Success
How to Satisfy Patients and Boost the Bottom Line

Elizabeth W. Woodcock, MBA, FACMPE, CPC

Medical Group Management Association
104 Inverness Terrace East
Englewood, CO 80112-5306
877.275.6462
mgma.com

Production Credits
Publisher/Senior Content Manager: Marilee E. Aust
Editorial and Production Manager: Anne Serrano, MA
Page Design, Composition, and Production: Glacier Publishing Services
Cover Design: Amy Kenreich and Brittany Hass, Studio Pattern

Library of Congress Cataloging-in-Publication Data

Woodcock, Elizabeth W.
  Front office success : how to satisfy patients and boost the bottom line / Elizabeth W. Woodcock.
      p. ; cm.
  Includes bibliographical references and index.
  Summary: "Front office operations are critical to optimize patient service and patient flow in a medical practice. The ideas, descriptions, and resources in this training guide are valuable whether your front office employees are new, changing duties, or looking for new ideas for roles they have been performing for many years"--Provided by publisher.
  ISBN 978-1-56829-379-0
  1. Medical offices--Management. I. Medical Group Management Association. II. Title.
  [DNLM: 1. Office Management--organization & administration. 2. Practice Management, Medical--organization & administration. W 80 W886f 2011]
  R728.W656 2011
  610.68--dc22
                          2010015779

Item #8253

ISBN: 978-1-56829-379-0

Printed in the United States of America
10 9 8 7 6 5 4 3 2 1

About MGMA

MGMA is the premier membership association for professional administrators and leaders of medical group practices. Since 1926, MGMA has delivered networking, professional education and resources, and political advocacy for medical practice management. Today, MGMA's 21,500 members lead 13,700 organizations nationwide in which some 275,000 physicians provide more than 40 percent of the healthcare services delivered in the United States.

MGMA's mission is to continually improve the performance of medical group practice professionals and the organizations they represent. MGMA promotes the group practice model as the optimal framework for healthcare delivery, assisting group practices in providing efficient, safe, patient-focused and affordable care. MGMA is headquartered in Englewood, Colo., and maintains a government affairs office in Washington, D.C.

About ACMPE

Founded in 1956, ACMPE is the standard-setting and certification organization of MGMA. Through ACMPE, medical group managers can earn the Certified Medical Practice Executive (CMPE) designation and go on to earn the highest distinction of Fellow in the ACMPE (FACMPE). ACMPE members belong to a network of management professionals dedicated to becoming the best in medical practice management by combining experience, learning, and professional certification.

Contents

Acknowledgments

. . . .

I would like to thank my husband and children for their continued support of the passion — and the countless hours — I channel into my professional endeavors.

Preface

As expenses soar and reimbursement declines, an efficient, effective, service-oriented front office staff is more important than ever. Although these staff members are key to a successful medical practice, the training time and effort dedicated to them, in most practices, is minimal at best. The operations of your front office are critical to optimize patient service and patient flow: this book serves to fill the need for training your front office staff to be more efficient and effective — all the while giving better service.

Creating a patient-centered front office was a benefit in yesteryear; today, it's essential.

MGMA is pleased to be a partner in delivering the skills, knowledge, and tools for front office training for medical practices.

About the Author

● ●

Elizabeth W. Woodcock, MBA, FACMPE, CPC, has visited countless medical practices in search of improving practice operations. Having observed front offices that work — and those that don't — she presents a training guide for performance improvement to enhance these essential team members. Believing that front office medical personnel are key players in a medical practice's success in marketing, patient loyalty, and earnings, she presents practical advice sure to guide front office personnel to become skilled and motivated team players.

Educated at Duke University (BA) and the Wharton School of Business (MBA), Elizabeth has traveled the country as an industry researcher, operations consultant, and expert presenter. Currently principal of Woodcock & Associates, Elizabeth has focused on medical practice operations throughout her career. She has served as the director of knowledge management for Physicians Practice Inc., a consultant with Medical Group Management Association's Health Care Consulting Group, group practice services administrator at the University of Virginia Health Services Foundation, and a senior associate at the Health Care Advisory Board.

Elizabeth is a Fellow in the American College of Medical Practice Executives (ACMPE). In addition to co-authoring *Operating Policies and Procedures Manual for Medical Groups* (1st, 2nd, 3rd, and 4th editions) and *The Physician Billing Process* (1st and 2nd editions), Elizabeth is the author of *Mastering Patient Flow* (1st, 2nd, and 3rd editions). A frequent contributor to national healthcare publications, she currently resides in Atlanta, Georgia, with her husband and three children.

To contact or learn more about Elizabeth, go to:
www.elizabethwoodcock.com.

About the Editor

Robert Redling, MS, is a freelance writer and editor whose focus is on the business of healthcare. Formerly senior writer and Web content editor writer at the Medical Group Management Association and practice management editor at Physicians Practice Inc., he is a graduate of San Diego State University and the University of Kansas, Lawrence, where he earned his Master's of Science in journalism. Robert has been a speechwriter for the American Academy of Family Physicians, and a reporter for wire services and newspapers. He and his wife currently live in Tacoma, Washington.

Introduction

Who should read this book?

This book is a training manual to assist front office employees in improving efficiency, effectiveness, and customer service. Employees may be in the position of receptionist, registrationist, scheduler, telephone operator, cashier, collector — and any of the host of other responsibilities assigned to the front office team. The ideas, descriptions, and resources in this book are of value whether you are new to your medical practice, are changing duties, or are simply looking for new ideas for roles you have been performing for many years.

This book is neither meant to be exclusively for a large practice nor for a small practice, nor is it specific to either specialty or primary care practices. It is an all-purpose training guide for front office employees.

How to use this book

Since this book is organized around the functions most commonly assigned to the front office, we hope you follow this path from beginning to end. However, because each section is organized around a critical function, you may find it convenient jump ahead to specific sections.

Self-assessment tools and worksheets are provided throughout this book. At the end of each chapter are quizzes (with answer keys in Appendix B) to reinforce the knowledge gained. Integrated into the chapters are terms you need to know, and many include scripts to use as models when performing important functions, such as collecting time-of-service payments or making appointment confirmation calls.

This book can be used as a refresher course for experienced employees, or as a training tool for staff members who are new to the practice, or even for those who are working in a medical practice or other healthcare setting for the very first time. Use these lessons for individual learning or as part of group exercises.

However you use this book, we hope you find it useful in transforming your front office team into a high-performing asset for your medical practice.

[CHAPTER 1]

Customer Service:
Making It a Personal Commitment

Think of the last time you were at the mall and walked into one of the stores. Now take a minute to read and answer these questions with a "yes" or a "no."

> ➤ Did staff members greet you with a friendly smile?

> ➤ Was the staff person helpful?

> ➤ Did they treat you like it was important to them that you were there?

> ➤ Did you feel like you had the salesperson's undivided attention?

> ➤ Were there any unpleasant surprises with the product or the service?

> ➤ Did the salesperson seem to know what he or she was doing?

> ➤ Was the service fast?

> ➤ Was it easy to pay for the product or service?

All of these questions can be applied to how patients interact with you and your fellow team members at the front office in a medical practice. The reasons patients come to the practice may be medical — and how well that part of the service encounter ensues is not in your hands. All the same, these questions are the basics of good service that can be directly influenced by *you*.

This book explains the many technical skills and areas of knowledge that help you be a success in the front office. Patient reception, registration, scheduling, telephones, cashiering, and collections are among the duties expected when working in the front office. However, success is more than being a worker clocking time. It depends on becoming a productive and supportive member of the front office *team*. This chapter explains the basics of good customer service as they apply to your important role in a medical practice.

Trends in customer service

As a member of the front office team in today's medical practice, you work at a time when patients have become much more demanding. It's part of a national trend for all customers to be more demanding; it's not just occurring in medical practices, it's happening in all businesses. People want more — and they want it faster. These greater expectations are thanks, in part, to the Internet: we expect to get more information, more quickly than our parents ever could and we expect to have a vast number of choices. Those demands carry over to all sectors of the economy. People are less likely to wait quietly these days when things run behind.

Demands of the front office

Receptionists, registrationists, schedulers, telephone operators, cashiers, and collectors — and those who perform all of those jobs — working on the "front lines" of the medical practice are asked to be high-performing multi-taskers who can:

- ➤ Greet patients;
- ➤ Register patients;
- ➤ Respond to patients' questions;
- ➤ Collect money;
- ➤ Answer telephones;

➤ Schedule appointments;

➤ Take messages;

➤ Keep an eye on the maintenance of the reception area; and

➤ Deal with unexpected delays in the daily schedule.

And, oh yes, do many of those things (and often more) at the same time — and do it all with a smile!

In this chapter, we look at the most important skill of high-performing front office staff. No, it isn't being a whiz at technology or working faster than everyone else. And it isn't something that you would necessarily pick up just by having lots of medical practice experience. This most important skill of all is providing good customer service.

Skill sets

Doing a great job as a front office team member requires several technical and interpersonal skills. You need to know how to use the practice management and electronic health records systems of your practice as well as its telephone, e-mail, and internal messaging systems. You also must be familiar with the registration process, collect money from patients at the time of service, and understand how to verify insurance eligibility, just to name a few. In sum, you have lots of technical skills to acquire!

As for interpersonal skills, you'll be challenged to make each patient feel welcomed, and remain calm and friendly even when you get flustered or in a rush. At times, you will be on the receiving end of the frustrations of patients who feel like they have been waiting too long to see their physician — or those challenged by limited financial resources. Most importantly, all of your customers aren't feeling their best — that's exactly why they're in front of you!

Don't get the idea that this is an impossible job. Or one that's a pain in the neck. In fact, many people love the almost infinite variety of tasks — small and large — that are part of working in the front office, and appreciate the opportunity to make a difference in someone's life.

If you want to learn about what makes your medical practice function as a viable business, if you like working with people — really, truly like people — and you get a charge out of seeing your efforts make a difference, then you're in the right job.

The Ten Commandments of Good Service

Customers today are often treated like they are a nuisance, instead of the reason that a company is in business at all. The same goes for patients coming to your medical practice. Capturing and keeping the loyalty of patients is a long-term challenge. It's something you must strive for every day and with every transaction and interaction, no matter how big or small. Follow these "Ten Commandments of Good Service" to keep loyal patients.

1. **Greet patients warmly and sincerely.** Try to personalize each encounter by greeting and acknowledging each patient. Why? Patients form lasting impressions of your practice as soon as they walk in the door or call on the telephone.

2. **Listen to patients.** Make sure patients have a chance to express their thoughts and feelings. Why? Whether it is a simple request or a complaint, patients want to feel like they are being treated as individuals.

3. **Use names.** Always introduce yourself and call patients by their desired address (Mr., Ms., or Mrs.) and name. Why? It's another way to make the encounter with your medical practice personal and memorable for patients.

4. **Be prepared to help patients.** Learn the front office procedures you are asked to perform and the technology you are

expected to use. Take time to understand more about your practice and how it works. Why? Seeing the bigger picture, and knowing why things are done the way they are and who to go to for help, better positions you as the patient's guide and advocate.

5. **Go the extra mile.** Closely linked to the previous commandment about being prepared, look for opportunities to show empathy and understanding and think of ways you can help patients navigate registration, waiting, and other processes. Why? It can make a lasting and positive impression on patients and help you enjoy your job more too.

6. **Show respect.** Keep patients informed about delays and apologize for them. Why? Staff members who show respect to patients help reinforce their impressions of your practice's service and, indeed, a good impression of its quality of care.

7. **Make time to de-stress.** Don't skip the lunch breaks or other short opportunities for downtime you might have. If things are really busy, then at least stand up, stretch, and take a few deep breaths when the opportunity arises (that is, without holding up patients who are registering). Keep a picture of your family and/or pet near your computer to look at; and remember that your patients are somebody's family member too. Why is it important to control stress? Because stress on the job leads to lower performance, fatigue, and a host of other problems that won't put you at your best.

8. **Avoid office politics and gossip.** Steer clear of gossiping about patients and other staff members. Avoid getting ensnarled in office politics, such as power struggles between employees. Why? Though they are hard to avoid, especially in a small office, gossiping and office politics destroy morale. Try to focus on what's best for patients — and your coworkers.

9. **Be a team member.** Be supportive of your coworkers, jump in to help when they need it, and take an interest in training and offering suggestions for improvements to your supervisor. Why? When coworkers can trust and respect each other, the

WORDS OF WISDOM

Tips for success from Mom

It's easy to be a success at customer service. Just remember what your mother taught you:

- Remember your manners:
  - Say "please," "thank you," and "may I;" and
  - Use "Mr." and "Ms.;" "Sir" and "Ma'am."
- Don't let personal issues intrude into your job.
- Arrive on time to work.
- Don't use the practice's property (computers, copiers, fax machines, postage meter, etc.) for personal reasons.
- Be gentle and respectful when disagreeing or criticizing.
- Do not gossip at work and don't gossip about your practice (its patients, physicians, or coworkers) with others directly, or on your Facebook or other social networking page.
- If you don't know, ask.
- Be presentable:
  - Keep work clothes neat, unwrinkled, and clean;
  - Don't wear strong-smelling perfumes or exude other body odors;
  - Avoid flashy jewelry or heavy makeup; and
  - Don't chew gum, eat food, or listen to music on headphones while on duty.
- Don't use your personal communications device (cellular phone, laptop, etc.) to send text messages, make personal calls, or visit social networking pages while at work.

As you can see, what your mother taught you really can help you succeed in the real world!

day runs much more smoothly and everyone is a winner —
patients, the physicians, your coworkers, and, most of all, you.

10. **Communicate.** Think of every interaction you have with
patients, coworkers, and your supervisor as an opportunity to get
things done and get them done right. Why? Communication
makes all types of businesses, including medical practices, run
better and serves their customers (patients) better.

Although these ten commandments can apply to many types of
business settings, they are especially important in a person-to-person
service setting like the medical practice.

The moment of truth

The "moment of truth" is a customer service concept. It refers to any
instance when a customer has an opportunity to make a judgment
about the quality of service you provide.

We talk more in Chapter 2, Reception, about the concept of the
"moment of truth" as it applies directly to your responsibility to
make patients feel welcomed to the practice. For the front office
team, there are many potential moments of truth:

➤ Telephone interactions;

➤ Body language and response when patients ask for something;

➤ Patience when patients are slow to find their insurance card or
other information; and

➤ Showing consideration when a patient has a special problem,
or perhaps just a fussy child.

The thing about moments of truth is that they can sneak up on you.
The offhand remark, the off-the-wall request, and so forth, all seem
to happen without warning. Instead of trying to plan for each possible moment of truth — there really are too many to list — consider
yourself in the mode of being the best host or hostess. The patients

are your guests and you want them to be comfortable and have everything they need while they are in your house.

Your practice itself also has several moments of truth. Many of these are out of your direct control. You didn't choose the outdated building your practice rents and maybe you would never have selected that wallpaper either. But you can influence how patients deal successfully with many aspects of your practice's physical layout, such as:

- **Parking.** Tell patients the best areas to park when they schedule appointments, and offer to validate parking lot receipts, if applicable.
- **Grounds.** Alert your supervisor to hazards that should be addressed, such as a loose handrail on stairs.
- **Door.** Get up and hold the door for feeble patients, a parent carrying a child, or, frankly, do it for every patient if time permits.
- **Signs.** Make sure they are neat and clean with all words spelled correctly, and not hung crooked or curling up with age.
- **Reception area.** Keep it clean and picked up with magazines in neat piles.
- **Front office.** Keep your work area orderly and desk tops as clear as possible.
- **Wayfinding.** Make sure patients understand where to go and how to get there.

The reason a moment of truth leaves such a lasting impression — positive or negative — is that many patients are doing something out of their normal routine when they visit your practice. It's all a new experience for them, so expect them to pay close attention to every detail of this interaction.

You are the moment of truth

With first impressions being so powerful and long lasting, you must always put your best foot forward. It can be the simplest thing: making direct eye contact, smiling, and speaking in a positive, enthusiastic manner when you greet a patient.

With automation and other cost management processes undermining the personal touch at every turn, people react all the more positively when someone makes them feel valued and appreciated. They'll want to return to your practice, instead of finding another one the next time they need to see a physician. And, just as important, they'll mention your practice when someone asks them to recommend a physician. Managing the moments of truth means you have a lot of power, so use it to show people that your practice embraces service and quality.

Body language counts

Watch your body language. Your body language conveys as much as the words you say. Maybe even more! When you talk to patients, make eye contact, smile, and lean slightly toward them. Doing this sends the message: "I really care about you!"

Sometimes our body language undermines what we are saying. For example, if you walk into a store and the clerk walks up to you, looks you in the eye, then smiles and says, "Hi, welcome to our store," you get the feeling that they are interested in helping you. Now suppose the clerk said the very same words but was staring at the ground with a slouched posture and had her arms crossed while she was talking. Do you get the impression that this person cares a bit about giving you good service? It's not always going to be that obvious, but you can send signals to patients that make them feel welcomed just by the way you stand or sit when you speak to them (see Exhibit 1.1).

[EXHIBIT 1.1]	Body language do's and don'ts

Do's	Don'ts
➤ **Arms:** comfortably at your sides ➤ **Eyes:** making contact with patient's ➤ **Facial expression:** friendly, smiling ➤ **Body position:** leaning toward patient (whether sitting or standing)	➤ **Arms:** crossed or hands in pockets ➤ **Eyes:** looking away (at a computer screen or paperwork) or looking down at the floor ➤ **Facial expression:** frowning, rolling eyes, or raising eyebrows when questions are asked ➤ **Body position:** leaning back, putting feet up on your workstation, slouching in chair, turning to the side while speaking to the patient

Professional appearance

Your appearance should be more than just adequate. It should be polished, but not in a style that patients might think is too flashy or just trying to impress. You should maintain clean hair, nails, and skin. Your clothing should be fresh, matching, and wrinkle-free. If your practice requires a uniform, order the correct size and make sure it's clean, unwrinkled, and unstained every morning.

Many medical practices have dress codes and other guidelines about the personal appearance of staff. In some cases, this is for the sake of appearances: patients put a lot of trust in their physicians, and everything they see in their physician's practice — including you — either supports or detracts from that impression. Other guidelines about dress are for safety reasons; for example, sturdy footwear with a low heel is a must because you may have to help escort a patient who is unsteady on his feet, so you need to be the surefooted one.

To create a professional image, some medical practices require all employees to wear a uniform, including those in the front office. A uniform takes all the guesswork, and perhaps most of the expense (if the practice pays or offers a stipend for uniforms), out of what to wear to work, saving you money and time.

Here are some tips to make sure you know what is best to wear in the medical practice setting.

Safe footwear. This is a safety concern as well as an appearance issue. Wear shoes (not sandals) that are closed-toe, medium or low heeled, with non-slip soles. Ask your supervisor for suggestions about styles, brands, and where to purchase work footwear.

Personal hygiene and appearance. Maintain clean personal hygiene and don't wear perfume.

Nails. Your fingernails should maintain the practice's professional image. Keep them clean, well manicured, and moderate in length.

Hair. Keep it clean, neatly trimmed, and contained so that it does not come in contact with patients. Hairstyle and hair color should support your practice's professional image.

Jewelry. It must be small and simple. It cannot obstruct your work, and should be visible on the ear only (that means no facial jewelry such as nose, eyebrow, lip, and other piercings).

Tattoos. Body art such as tattoos must be covered at all times while on duty.

These and other standards guiding staff appearance are part of the approach medical practices take to present an image of professional care.

FYI

Dress code policy

Here is a typical policy that medical practices use. Your practice's policy may be similar.

> *It is the policy of Medical Practice Associates to require every employee to dress professionally and appropriately for his or her position. Each employee represents Medical Practice Associates to its patients, vendors, and visitors. Because of our responsibility to inspire confidence in our professionalism and high quality of care, employees are expected to wear appropriate dress as defined herein. Each employee is expected to reflect the organization's standards through professional dress, grooming, conduct, language, and decorum.*

Source: Woodcock, Elizabeth W., and Bette A. Warn. 2011. *Operating Policies and Procedures Manual for Medical Practices, 4th Ed.* Reprinted with permission from the Medical Group Management Association, 104 Inverness Terrace East, Englewood, Colorado 80112. 877.ASK.MGMA, www.MGMA.com. Copyright 2011.

Handling stress

Working in the front office puts you on the front lines of interaction with patients. This can be stressful at times. Here are some suggestions to handle the stressful times.

Be organized. It can be very stressful when you can't find the piece of paper, folder, message, or other required information when you need it. At the beginning of each day, spend five or ten minutes to tidy and organize your work area, and make sure you know where everything is for the day. (See Chapter 2, Reception, for more details on getting ready for the day.)

Take breaks when you get them. It's possible that the crush of patients might make you work through the lunch hour at times. Hopefully, that is not a regular event. Fight the urge to come back early from your lunch break to "get a head start" on work. Cutting short your break times may improve your productivity in the short term, but in the long run, you could end up more stressed and eventually burned-out.

Avoid getting involved in office gossip and office politics. It is stressful enough at times in a medical practice, so why add more stress by tearing people down or just idly complaining?

Take mini-breaks. Whenever there are a few seconds between tasks, get up and walk around to stretch your legs. If you are stuck at a desk for hours at a time, get a drink of water, pick up documents from the printer or fax machine, or perform some other duty that allows you to move around a bit.

Sometimes stress is unavoidable, but proactively managing it means that you can keep it in check. If you do, stress is much less likely to ruin your day (and your health).

Even though these tips are useful in making office stress easier to handle, it also is imperative that you learn to anticipate and deal with the things that create a stressful environment in the first place. It would be nice to think that everyone in the healthcare field could extend their compassion for patients to their coworkers too and never do or say anything that causes stress to anyone else. But, in fact, it is because most healthcare workers have high goals to provide quality medical care that they sometimes get frustrated with each other.

WORDS OF WISDOM

Handling difficult patients (and difficult coworkers)

➤ Breathe!

➤ Put the situation in perspective.

➤ Recognize your feelings.

➤ Do NOT take it personally.

➤ Suspend judgment.

➤ Obtain assistance if needed.

➤ After the event, don't engage others (that is, don't starting gossiping about it).

Office politics

What's so bad about office politics, gossip, and nitpicking? Everything! These issues:

➤ **Put people in a bad mood.** Patients can detect the tension.

➤ **Reduce customer service quality.** Good patient service in the front office requires a lot of cooperation. When people are not working well together, they are less likely to go the extra mile for each other to help resolve problems.

➤ **Distract everyone's attention.** Your focus should be first and foremost on how to make the patient in front of you feel welcomed and how to help that person. That's harder to do when office politics cause your mind to be elsewhere.

➤ **Add to stress.** Daily conflicts with coworkers sap your energy and hurt your job performance.

Office politics is something that many of us have to learn how to deal with in order to ensure our longevity and success at the office.

Try these tips to deal with people who gossip, play favorites, or try to make other people look bad:

> Walk away or refuse to participate in conversations that are mean spirited or involve nonbusiness news about other workers.

> Focus on your willingness to grow and learn new things when talking to your supervisor, instead of complaining about being overlooked.

> Try to be positive in your outlook and comments.

> Act respectful and professional in your dealings with coworkers — treat them with the same consideration you would patients.

Think of office politics as simply how the differences between people are playing out in the workplace. Differences in opinions, and conflicts of work styles and personalities often show up as office politics. To successfully navigate office politics, pay attention to building good communications and relationships with those around you.

Positive steps to get ahead

A big part of seizing the moment of truth involves taking action on your own — being proactive. This doesn't mean breaking rules, but you should do something positive to solve a problem or prevent one from happening. Being proactive — within the boundaries of your assigned job — pleases patients, impresses supervisors, and helps coworkers who don't always step in to fix the problem or bail you out. It can even improve your job satisfaction.

Try examining your work style and your approach to work in the medical practice by answering the questions in Exhibits 1.2, 1.3, and 1.4 with "yes," "no," or "sometimes." Think back to specific encounters you've had with patients, coworkers, and supervisors as you answer the questions.

[EXHIBIT 1.2]			**Personal proactivity self-test**
Yes	No	Sometimes	**What are your answers to these questions about being proactive? (Mark each one: "yes," "no," or "sometimes.")**
			Do I listen carefully to patients who have a question, problem, or special request?
			Do I try to understand the viewpoint and concerns patients are feeling when they have questions, problems, or special requests?
			Do I verify with patients that I correctly heard their question, problem, or special request before I try to resolve it?
			Do I try to take action when patients have a question, problem, or special request that I can't answer or resolve immediately?
			Do I know to whom to turn when I don't know the answer or how to resolve a patient's question, problem, or special request?
			Do I look upon patient questions, problems, and special requests as part of my responsibility to help answer or solve?
			Do I go the extra mile to help coworkers and patients even if I know my supervisor might not notice my efforts?
			Do I accept the blame when someone in another part of the medical practice has caused a misunderstanding or inconvenience for the patient?
			Do I look for opportunities to give outstanding service to the patients I encounter in the front office?

Questions you answered with "no" or "sometimes" are behaviors, attitudes, or work habits that you need to change to become a top performer. Keep in mind that all of these are areas that your supervisor, coworkers, or patients have likely noticed about you and your performance.

[EXHIBIT 1.3]			**Teamwork self-test**

Yes	No	Sometimes	What are your answers to these questions about teamwork? (Mark each one: "yes," "no," or "sometimes.")
			Do I keep track of the concerns patients tell me about and transmit them to my supervisor?
			Do I recommend my ideas to improve service to my supervisor?
			Do I consider myself part of the medical practice's public image?
			Do I volunteer to help on projects or to help my coworkers who have a lot of extra work to do?
			Do I step forward to help clean, straighten up, and fix things even though it is not one of my direct responsibilities?
			Do I seek out training when it is available that can help me do my job better?
			Do I participate in staff meetings when there is an opportunity to speak up, answer questions, or make suggestions?
			Do I help my coworkers when they do not understand a new procedure, skill, or technology?

Questions that you answered with "no" or "sometimes" are behaviors, attitudes, or work habits that you need to change to be a top performer. Keep in mind that all of these areas are ones that your supervisor, coworkers, or patients have likely noticed about you and your performance.

Teamwork

Teamwork is communicating and sharing information with your coworkers and supervisor. It can mean taking a few seconds to remind the other receptionist that the physician is returning late from lunch that afternoon. It could mean passing along a tip about the practice management system that helps others. Teamwork also is stepping in to assist coworkers or your supervisor when you don't

[EXHIBIT 1.4]			**Personal success self-test**

Yes	No	Sometimes	What are your answers to these questions about personal success? (Mark each one: "yes," "no," or "sometimes.")
			Do I know where my job description is and have I looked at it lately?
			Do I understand the performance standard for my position?
			Do I accept constructive criticism from my supervisor and try to use it to improve?
			Do I keep my supervisor informed of my successes?
			Do I read the training materials, announcements, and other information I am given by my supervisor?

Questions that you answered with "no" or "sometimes" are behaviors, attitudes, or work habits that you need to change to be a top performer. Keep in mind that all of these areas are ones that your supervisor, coworkers, or patients have likely noticed about you and your performance.

really have to, such as volunteering to help stuff the new practice brochures into envelopes for an upcoming mailing when you have time between patients or telephone calls (see Exhibit 1.3.).

Success in business today requires that your entire organization focus on common objectives. A commitment to teamwork can help increase office productivity because it gives everyone a shared sense of purpose. A good team is one that pulls together the work of individual staff members — even when they have different perspectives and skills — and encourages them to perform better.

Personal success

There's more to work than just showing up. With the stresses of fast-changing technology and more demands for efficiency, your practice needs your help. You can help yourself get ahead and help your practice by making an effort to learn and understand more about your job and how to do it better (see Exhibit 1.4).

Conclusion

The medical practice for which you work needs many things to succeed: good physicians, convenient location, favorable insurance contracts, skilled staff, but most of all, it needs loyal patients. Loyal patients come back even when they could go to another physician's office. Loyal patients also recommend the medical practice and its physicians to their friends. Your practice needs both loyal patients and a stream of new patients to stay in business.

Customer service is the human touch that makes your medical practice your patients' first choice for their care. It helps patients feel connected with your medical practice. The key to building patient loyalty is excellent customer service. And the person who can provide it is *you*.

CHAPTER 1 QUIZ

True or False

Circle the correct answer.

1. One of the reasons that patients expect to get information fast from medical practices is because they have become accustomed to getting information and service quickly via the Internet. T   F

2. The ability to provide good customer service is not usually expected of front office staff. T   F

3. Staff members who show respect and consideration are giving patients a good impression of the practice. T   F

4. A practical tip for better performance as a front office staff member is to not let personal issues intrude into your job. T   F

5. Alerting your supervisor when you notice hazards that could harm patients, such as a loose handrail on stairs, isn't really an important part of customer service for front office staff. T   F

6. Slouching, looking down at the floor, and folding your arms across your chest are examples of negative body language. T   F

Multiple Choice

Choose the one correct answer to each question.

1. The duties expected of front office staff typically include:
   a. Greeting patients
   b. Registering patients
   c. Answering telephones
   d. All of the above

2. The single most important skill of an effective front office staff member is providing:
   a. Injections
   b. Good customer service
   c. Medical advice to patients
   d. None of the above

3. It is important for front office staff to learn to manage job stress because:
   a. Stress can cause fatigue and lower performance
   b. Stress reduction is required by law
   c. Stress can make you feel energetic
   d. All of the above

4. Being presentable in the front office means:
   a. Keeping work clothes neat, unwrinkled, and clean
   b. Not wearing strong-smelling perfumes
   c. Avoiding flashy jewelry and heavy makeup
   d. All of the above

5. Which of these is NOT a recommended way to impress patients when greeting them?
   a. Making direct eye contact
   b. Keeping your head down to focus on completing other work before greeting the patient
   c. Smiling
   d. Speaking in a positive, enthusiastic manner

6. Tips to correctly deal with patients who are complaining are to:
   a. Put the situation in perspective
   b. Not take it personally
   c. Obtain assistance if needed
   d. All of the above

Matching

Enter the letter of the correct definition from the right column next to the term in the left column that is the best match.

1. __ Teamwork
2. __ Proactive
3. __ Office politics
4. __ Safe footwear
5. __ Dress code
6. __ Moment of truth

a. Small event that leaves a lasting impression.
b. Guidelines about what to wear for professional appearance and safety.
c. Taking action to solve a problem or prevent one from happening.
d. Puts everyone in a bad mood and raises stress.
e. Closed-toe with non-slip soles.
f. Assisting coworkers or supervisor when you don't have to.

Answers to this quiz are in Appendix B.

[CHAPTER 2]

Reception:
The Patient Has Arrived, Now What?

Walk into a McDonald's, a Starbucks, or another national franchise food chain and stand in front of the counter. More than likely, you won't stand there very long before a worker behind the counter asks if you've been helped yet. Now think back to the last time you were in a restaurant when the waiter or waitress kept passing by your table time after time without making eye contact. You might like the food at that restaurant, but you also know that bad service can ruin a good meal. You might even start avoiding the place altogether at peak hours which, unfortunately, tend to be the meal times when you'd most like to eat.

The important responsibilities of patient reception include greeting patients warmly and making them feel acknowledged. Successfully completing the administrative tasks to which you are assigned initiates the patient's encounter at your medical practice, but good patient service starts earlier — when the patient walks in the door — just as it does when the customer walks into McDonald's or Starbucks.

Success in reception services requires customer skills, but also attention to detail, work efficiency, and knowledge of the required tasks. You will be called upon to use good judgment, exercise basic common sense, react calmly under pressure, and, depending on how your practice's reception process works, multi-task and make certain types of decisions within boundaries set by your supervisor.

You are the face of the practice

The reception area represents your medical practice and so do you and the service you provide. You are in a powerful position to enhance how patients perceive your practice.

Your first interaction with patients sets the stage for how they look at the entire organization. In just a few seconds, your greeting, attitude, and words make patients feel welcomed or make them wonder if maybe they couldn't find another practice to go to next time.

 WORDS OF WISDOM

Qualities of success at reception

- Friendly to patients
- Shows common sense
- Remains calm and efficient under pressure
- Able to juggle multiple tasks
- Makes good decisions

Greeting the patient

There probably isn't a receptionist around who doesn't claim to greet patients, but we've all observed many suboptimal interactions by receptionists. Unfriendly and inefficient check-in staff and processes irritate patients before they've even taken a seat in your reception area. A bad attitude can spread like the flu. A bad attitude in one part of the practice will be felt in other areas as well, and soon everyone's day is a little more stressful.

Your responsibilities in receiving patients effectively include:

- Greeting arriving patients — don't just check them in like a package the delivery service just dropped off; receive them as you would want to be received.

➤ Using patients' names and making eye contact — every time.

➤ Proactively keeping patients informed about delays.

How do you know that your best attempt at a warm and sincere greeting is getting across? Sometimes you won't know for sure. Some patients are sick and worried, so it can be hard to "read" their reactions.

One of the best ways to get across a warm and sincere greeting is to say "thanks." In other words, look for opportunities to thank patients for choosing your physician's medical practice. It only makes sense to express this appreciation because that patient's decision to come to your practice helps pay your salary. The more you can feel appreciative that a person has decided to come to your physician, the more natural it will feel to help them. And that kind of sincerity will be noticed.

WORDS OF WISDOM

Why names are so important

Using a person's name shows respect — and it proves that you are listening to them. Use names:

At the beginning of a conversation:
"Ms. Jones, I'd be happy to take care of that for you."

At the end of a conversation:
"Please stop by the lab, Ms. Jones."

During the conversation:
"We'll have those results to you, Ms. Jones, by next Friday."

Rule of thumb: You can never use the patient's name too often!

Reception services workstation requirements

➤ Computer with practice management and electronic health record systems

➤ All necessary forms

➤ Telephone

➤ Desktop scanner or photocopier

➤ Daily schedule (manual or automated)

➤ Office supplies

➤ Communication tool for patient arrival

➤ Practice policies and procedures

➤ Physician rotation list and patient priority list

Remember, it isn't just having the right tools, it's knowing where they are and how to use them. Organization and neatness count.

Balancing service and tasks

When patients arrive at your practice, you are probably not the first contact they have had with your practice. Some patients have been in the office before. Many scheduled their appointment by telephone. Most received another contact with the practice through a confirmation call that reminded them when to come and what to bring to the appointment. A few had the appointment made for them by another physician's office, as in the case of being referred by a primary care physician to a specialist. But for many patients, this is the first *face-to-face* contact they have with your practice.

First impressions are formed quickly — experts reveal that an impression is made in less than 10 seconds — but last for a long time. It's critical to make the patient feel welcomed. The special challenge of working at the front office is that you must pay careful attention to details and complete the many important clerical tasks you've been assigned. In concert with these essential responsibilities, you also must provide good service.

Balancing tasks and people

Performing your duties requires you to balance technical skills with people skills. Attention to courtesy helps keep "patients patient" when physicians are running late. Most importantly, your courteousness keeps patients satisfied. Staff manners and courtesy play a big role in whether patients are willing to come back to your practice or choose another one.

Too many times, front office personnel are so focused on their many tasks that they forget about customer service. Don't assume that patients come to your practice because they have no other choices. In most communities, medical practices have plenty of competition. Don't believe that there is an endless supply of new patients waiting to get in. If you deliver service that wows patients, you'll find that they not only come back, but they also spread the good word about the great experience they had at your practice.

You can make a difference

Your greatest challenge of all — always providing good service, even to patients who may not show appreciation — may be the one that offers the greatest rewards. Your patients are not always happy when they arrive at the office — they may be sick themselves, they may be caring for sick children, parents, or loved ones, and they are probably tired and anxious. You can assume that every patient entering the office wishes that time would pass, and pass quickly. The fact is, you don't *have* to smile and you don't *have* to be nice. Most patients

WORDS OF WISDOM

Signs that an unfriendly check-in experience is about to happen

Put yourself in the patient's shoes. What would you think if you saw the following when you walked into your personal physician's office?

➤ Employees sitting at the front office eating snacks and gossiping about patients while on break.

➤ A "take-a-number" system for registration.

➤ The sign-in sheet on a ledge outside a closed sliding window with a notice on the window saying, "Ring the bell if you need help."

➤ The triage nurse talking to a patient on the telephone about a medical problem within earshot of the patients sitting in the reception area.

➤ Completed forms or other paperwork from patients laying on top of the reception services ledge.

➤ Urine samples sitting on the front office counter.

➤ Patients standing at the check-in counter while employees talk to one another.

➤ The receptionist pointing to a clipboard and mumbling, "Sign in," without even looking up.

➤ Staff frequently interrupting conversations with patients to answer telephones.

➤ Staff at the reception area not looking up to greet patients as they enter the practice.

➤ Reception staff acting flustered and speaking to coworkers disrespectfully.

These behaviors send the message to patients: "we take you for granted." Sadly, the list of poor check-in practices witnessed in medical practices, large and small, new and established, could go on for many pages. Let's just say there is room for improvement in all practices.

who are not feeling well are not expecting much; they just want to be seen and go home. This makes your job more difficult, but in the darkest times, being a ray of optimism can truly make a difference in a patient's life. Even if a patient doesn't return the smile, your smile does makes a difference.

Preparation

One of the biggest reasons front office staff fail to give good service or greet patients properly is because they are flustered by last-minute details. It is hard to be gracious and calm when it feels like you've got so many fires to put out and more unexpected tasks keep popping up.

More and more medical practices try to calm the atmosphere and make things run smoother by trying to anticipate problems. They do this by establishing a daily preparation checklist (see Appendix 2A), previewing patients' charts (see Appendix 2B), and holding mandatory five-minute "huddles" for staff before office hours commence. These quick stand-up meetings can give everyone a rundown of what's going to happen that session or day. If you are not included in these daily morning huddles, be sure to get a quick summary of the important issues that will impact you. These can include an appointment cancellation made because the patient was admitted to the hospital during the night — that means there is an opening now in the daily schedule that can be filled with a patient who calls in asking to be seen on the same day. Or that opening might be filled by someone on your practice's waiting list of patients who want to get in sooner. It might be your job to call those patients. Regardless of the particulars of the situation, preparing for the day can keep you calm, focused, and successful.

Skills development

To be part of an outstanding front office team, look for ways to
develop your skills in:

> ➤ **Multi-tasking.** You must be capable of greeting patients,
> checking them in, collecting their money, answering the tele-
> phone, and giving a message to a clinical assistant — all with
> a smile.

> ➤ **Task knowledge.** You need intimate knowledge of the prac-
> tice management and electronic health records systems, as
> well as the telephone, e-mail, and internal messaging systems.

> ➤ **Teamwork.** Think of yourself as a partner with the practice's
> business office and clinical team, facilitating the information
> that makes — or breaks — their jobs.

Conclusion

You are an important member of the practice's team: your service
and behavior in the front office helps form patients' perceptions
that the practice is well run and that they will receive high-quality,
professional care.

Appendix 2A: Daily preparation checklist

• •

Preparation makes the day run smoother. Front office employees likely have many small tasks to do at the beginning of the day. Instead of leaving it all to memory, you can use a checklist to make sure everything gets done, and done correctly. Here's a sample checklist that you can edit or add to as needed to get each day off to a good start in your practice.

Daily checklist: getting prepared for the day

❑ Arrive at least 15 minutes before the first patient is due to check in.

❑ Check the outside mailbox for mail.

❑ Unlock the door.

❑ Turn on lights in the front office and reception areas.

❑ Inspect appearance of the reception area; straighten magazines, furniture, etc.

❑ Turn off call forwarding, and check with the answering service for messages. Record messages, routing them electronically or manually to the appropriate person.

❑ Review the automated confirmation call report. Mark "cancels" on the schedule, putting a copy on the nurses' station or communicating electronically to alert them of the newly opened appointment slots.

❑ Adjust heating/air-conditioning thermostat.

❑ Review the inventory of supplies and forms for the day. Retrieve additional supplies if necessary.

❑ Unlock the cash drawer. Verify that the opening balance ($100) and cash log are present.

❑ If applicable, verify that all patient records are pulled for today's schedule. In the event of a missing chart, attempt to locate it. If it cannot be located, create a shadow chart to include printing any information electronically.

❏ Familiarize yourself with the past due account list.

❏ Greet patients by name, with a smile and direct eye contact, making them feel welcome. Register and arrive patients as they present.

Appendix 2B: Sample chart preparation

Members of the front office team may be asked to help prepare the medical charts of patients who have appointments in the upcoming day or session. A checklist ensures that you do a comprehensive job. Here's a sample to use to develop your own checklist.

Sample Chart Prep	
Step 1: Review the record to ensure that previous documentation has been filed, recorded, and/or scanned and is in place.	
Step 2: Scan the previous dictation; look for orders.	
Did the physician request a consult with another physician (for example, referred the patient to a cardiologist)?	*Check for referring physician letters/ documentation.*
Did the physician order a lab test?	*Check for test results.*
Did the physician order a radiological test or procedure?	*Check for films and interpretation.*
Did the patient have a procedure or surgery since the last visit?	*Check for procedure or operative report.*
Did the patient communicate with your practice since the last visit?	*Check for telephone message form.*
Step 3: Physician-specific protocols [to be completed by physician].	
1.	
2.	
3.	

CHAPTER 2 QUIZ

True or False

Circle the correct answer.

1. As a receptionist, your service and the reception area itself often give patients their first impressions of the medical practice. **T   F**

2. Using the patient's name is not really an important part of greeting or making them feel respected. **T   F**

3. Organization and neatness are important elements of an efficient front office. **T   F**

4. At most medical practices, the patients come because it's their only option. **T   F**

5. Patients standing at the check-in counter while employees talk to one another is a sign of an unfriendly check-in experience. **T   F**

Multiple Choice

Choose the one correct answer to each question.

1. Which of these is NOT listed in this chapter as a skill for success in patient reception services?
   a. Good customer service skills
   b. Training to administer allergy tests
   c. Attention to detail
   d. Good judgment

2. Responsibilities in greeting patients include:
   a. Greeting patients in a friendly but respectful manner
   b. Keeping patients informed about delays
   c. Using patients' names to show respect
   d. All of the above

3. Reception services workstation requirements include which of the following:
   a. Telephone
   b. Computer
   c. Daily schedule
   d. All of the above

4. Experts say that first impressions are formed in less than:
   a. A nanosecond
   b. 10 seconds
   c. 30 minutes
   d. 24 hours

5. In a medical practice, a "huddle" is a:
   a. Short meeting with staff before office hours to preview the session or day
   b. Football term that has nothing to do with medical offices
   c. Medical procedure
   d. None of the above

6. Important skills as a member of an outstanding front office team include:
   a. An ability to ignore patient complaints
   b. Willingness to keep news of delays from patients
   c. Multi-tasking, task knowledge, and teamwork
   d. All of the above

Matching

Enter the letter of the correct definition from the right column next to the term in the left column that is the best match.

1. __ Multi-tasking
2. __ Daily checklist
3. __ Teamwork
4. __ Front office responsibilities
5. __ Patient greeting requirement

a. Using name and making eye contact.
b. Working as a partner with your practice's business office, clinical team, and your coworkers.
c. Answering telephones and greeting patients.
d. Ability to do several things and do them well.
e. List of things to do at the start of each day.

Answers to this quiz are in Appendix B.

CHAPTER 3

Registration:
The Process of Enrolling Patients

You can walk into the dry cleaners, the pharmacy, or just about any other business on the planet and — if you are lucky — get the service you want without a lot of paperwork and signing of forms. Unfortunately, a medical practice cannot offer that sort of instant service, primarily because it has to know information about its customers, such as:

➤ Their identity;

➤ Their contact information;

➤ Their insurance coverage;

➤ Whether they have necessary authorizations for certain services;

➤ Their ability to pay and how much they may owe already for previous services; and

➤ How much they are expected to pay before receiving services.

Registering patients is more than getting them to sign on a clipboard or fill out a few forms. It is a carefully planned process of multiple actions. Accomplishing the steps that your practice has established for its registration protocols must be done accurately and with no activity missed. The information you gather here is used to properly identify patients, determine their insurance coverage, and file an insurance claim for your physician's services. A misstep here can mean a delay or even a loss of funds that your practice has rightfully earned.

Review the principles of registration discussed here and be sure you know how to complete every step of your own practice's registration process as well.

Registration process

Unlike many other types of businesses that provide services, there are a number of tasks to perform before a patient can be served. This process — registration — is enrolling the patient at your practice. The actual duties vary by practice. They may be different based on the physician's specialty, the types of patient served, and the structure of the practice. Each practice has its own protocols, but the process always includes gathering demographic and insurance information from the patient.

New patients

New patients typically take longer to register because of the additional information, forms, practice policies, and so forth, they must read, complete, and/or sign. Although some practices wait until the patient arrives, many practices perform some or all of the registration process *before* the patient presents. Performing registration tasks before a patient arrives is referred to as "pre-registration."

Pre-registration

Pre-registration makes for a more efficient work flow when it comes to checking in patients. It decreases the transaction time required by you in the front office after they arrive. In other words, the patient can get through the front office and back to the exam room faster.

Pre-registration is a process commonly used for new patients, but some practices pre-register all patients to ensure accurate, timely demographic and insurance information. Why? It is possible that patients have changed insurance companies, addresses, or telephone numbers since their last visit. Patients might also have changed employers, or they may have other important information changes. Any of these changes may affect what you and the rest of your team must do to handle that patient's records, billing, financial responsibility, referral(s), prescription(s), and so forth.

Pre-registration also reduces annoying paperwork for the patient. Handing a stack of papers to patients to complete in the reception area confirms in the patients' minds that they will be waiting for a while. A lengthy registration process can create a backup of patients and paperwork at the front office. This backup impedes a patient's journey in the practice and delays other patients from checking in. Another reason for pre-registration is that patients may not bring with them the necessary items to complete the paperwork, such as an insurance card. Finally, patients may rush through the forms to try to gain faster access to the provider they are scheduled to see. As they speed through the forms, they are more likely to not enter important information or make mistakes.

Your practice may ask you to pre-register patients over the telephone. Alternatively, you may be assigned to help patients pre-register via the practice's Website or Web-based patient portal, or through a kiosk in the reception area. Regardless of how it is performed, the benefits of pre-registration are more accurate information, a less anxious patient and a smoother work flow for everyone at the practice.

Registration information

Attention to detail at this early point in the patient flow process is critical. Whether you register patients before they present or when they present, important details that you need to gather and enter into the practice management system are in two areas: the patient's identity (also called demographics) and information related to the patient's insurance. Recording incorrect or incomplete information at this point likely means more work for you and your team members.

Ask the patient to complete or review — and correct as needed — information on the registration form that lists basic demographic and insurance information. Forms for each scheduled patient may be printed out the day before or at the time of the visit from your practice management system, or the information can be made available electronically for the patient to confirm. Each practice has its own forms and protocols. Some may want the patient to review each item at every visit; others just want to check that key items, such as name and date of birth, are correctly listed.

New patients should be asked to show an insurance card and identification. Photocopying these to either scan into the practice management system or store on paper in a file is a wise practice — medical identity theft is on the rise.

Exhibit 3.1 shows the key items that you may need to either record or confirm during the registration process about patients visiting the practice.

Your practice may require additional information to be gathered during registration, such as confirming benefits eligibility, querying about the patient's unmet deductible, or gathering the details related to the patient's employer if the patient's injury was sustained at work.

The registration process often concludes with the preparation of an encounter form for physicians to record the service(s) they perform. This form, which is also referred to as a charge ticket or superbill, needs to reflect accurate demographic and insurance information because the clinical staff often rely on it to make decisions about where to refer patients for testing, ancillary services, and specialty care. Attach the encounter form to the patient's chart if using a paper system; confirm the data if using an electronic records system.

EXHIBIT 3.1	Details of patient registration	
Information	**Reason(s)**	**Frequency (typical)**
Patient name matches practice's record	Correct medical record and correct billing	Each visit
Patient identity matches practice's record	Correct medical record and correct billing; reduction of business risk related to identity theft	At first visit to practice, at minimum
Information about the guarantor's insurance coverage	Correct billing	Detailed information at first visit to practice; request to update each visit
Confirmation of coverage and benefits directly with the insurance company ("insurance verification")	Correct billing; financial interest of the practice	Each visit
Patient address and telephone numbers	Correct billing and follow-up contact for medical care	Each visit
Co-payment	Insurance contract may require collection; financial interest of the practice	Each visit
HIPAA policy acknowledgment	Federal law	At first visit to practice
Practice policies and procedures, including financial policy	Financial interest of the practice	At first visit to practice, and with introduction of new policies and procedures
Assignment of benefits	Insurance contract, to allow the practice to bill and receive payment on behalf of the patient	At first visit to practice, and with change in insurance
Coinsurance, unmet deductible, outstanding account balance, and/or minimum deposits	Financial interest of the practice	Each visit: Can be done in front office or check-out. May require confirmation directly with the patient's insurance company and/or consultation with business office staff
If applicable, insurance pre- authorizations, referrals, waivers, and other confirmation of insurance coverage or patient responsibility	Insurance contract; correct billing; financial interest of the practice	Confirm at patient check-in on day of service (usually these are facilitated in advance)

[EXHIBIT 3.2]	Front office accuracy can make or break the practice
If you gather...	**The result may be...**
Inaccurate/missing information about the patient's insurance (for example, inaccurate insurance plan group number)	The patient's insurance company may deny payment.
Inaccurate patient address	Patient billing statements may be delayed or never received.
Incorrect telephone number	Patient can't be reached with important test results.
Wrong birth date or name misspelled	The patient's insurance company may deny payment, the patient's record can't be located, and care may be delayed while the patient's chart is located and confirmed.

It's important for you to work with your supervisor to discuss the information that needs to be gathered. In conjunction with your supervisor, develop a checklist of key items needed for registration and post it at your workstation.

If you don't register patients completely and accurately, there are significant negative implications for your fellow staff members — and patients (see Exhibit 3.2.)

The information you gather from patients needs to be accurate so that your practice runs smoothly. Ultimately, this goal also helps the patient: it improves the success of that patient's experience with your practice. If you collect and confirm accurate information, then the patient can successfully be reached with test results, the insurance company can adjudicate the claim correctly, and the patient recognizes how to effectively communicate with the practice and access future care.

Necessary signatures

There are a number of forms that patients must acknowledge and sign during the registration process. Many of these forms are signed when the patient registers as a new patient — one time only. Others must be renewed at each visit. Typically, these forms are handled and confirmed by the front office staff, so it's important for you to understand what they are and why they are required.

The most common forms that require the patient's signature are listed here. Your practice may use these forms — or others. Familiarize yourself with the forms that your practice requires.

> **Assignment of Benefits.** The patient agrees to assign his or her insurance benefits to your practice. This allows your practice to bill the insurance company and receive payment on the patient's behalf. Without this agreement, your practice might experience long delays in getting reimbursed by insurance companies for services. This form should be signed by every new patient as well as when they change insurance companies. Many practices establish a process to capture the assignment at every encounter.

> **Medical Records Release.** The patient agrees to permit the practice to release medical records on his or her behalf to third parties. This includes medical documentation requested by insurance companies when a claim is disputed. The form should be signed by new patients and upon change of insurance, at a minimum.

> **Waiver forms.** These waiver forms should be signed only when circumstances dictate. In most cases, waiver forms are used when the patient's insurance company does not cover the services to be rendered to the patient and, therefore, the patient is expected to pay. These forms do not guarantee payment but only set the expectation that the patient must pay.

> • **Insurance Coverage Waiver** is used for patients when their insurance coverage cannot be verified.

- **Non-Covered Services** form should be only used when the patient is to receive services that the physician believes will not be covered by the insurance company. Some insurance companies maintain their own forms for this purpose, such as Medicare's Advance Beneficiary Notice (ABN). An ABN is a written notification made to a Medicare beneficiary before they get items or services that the physician believes Medicare will not pay for. This form is usually offered by the clinical staff when the service is being provided, but it is good for the front office staff to be aware of this form in case a patient mentions it.

➤ **Financial Policy.** Many practices use a form to outline the practice's billing and payment policies. Patients are asked to sign the form to acknowledge their understanding of and agreement with the practice's financial policies.

➤ **Notice of Privacy Release**. The privacy regulations of the federal Health Insurance Portability and Accountability Act (HIPAA) require physicians to ask patients to acknowledge that they have been informed of the practice's HIPAA policies. This is not a consent form; rather it is an acknowledgment.

The forms patients are asked to read and sign by your practice do many things. They establish the rights of patients to the protection of their personal health information and other rights that might be required by law. These forms also give the ability to your practice to perform actions such as sharing patients' health information with their own insurance company, holding patients responsible for the costs of their medical care, and so on. Some forms are required by federal or state law or by insurance companies with which you have a contract. Be sure to obtain the signatures required by your practice and know how to explain the forms in case patients ask for clarification.

FYI

Explaining forms

The forms required for the patient to review and sign are complex. To reduce confusion, it pays to develop a script you can use with each form.

Example:

This is a copy of our Privacy Notice. It describes in detail how your personal health information is used and secured here at Family Medicine Associates. Please take it with you and read it at your convenience.

I also need you to sign this Acknowledgment Form stating that I gave you a copy of our Privacy Notice. This Acknowledgment Form will be placed in your medical record. It's our way of knowing we have given the Privacy Notice to every patient we treat.

You are welcome to pick up a copy of our Privacy Notice whenever you like on subsequent visits, but you only need to sign the Acknowledgment Form once.

Benchmarks

Every medical practice is different, but registering a patient typically takes five to eight minutes from start to finish. That's an average, however. It can take just two minutes or less to register established patients who have no changes to their demographic or insurance information, yet up to 14 minutes for new patients. At these rates, you could register between 60 and 80 patients per day, including getting all of the necessary insurance verifications, information updates, new patient registrations, collecting payments, and greeting patients.

[EXHIBIT 3.3]	Registration services staff benchmarks
Practice operations task	**Workload range**
Pre- or site registration with insurance verification	60–80 patients per day
Check-in with registration verification only	100–130 patients per day
Site check-in with registration verification and cashiering only	75–100 patients per day

©2011 Elizabeth W. Woodcock, MBA, FACMPE, CPC

If your practice verifies insurance information in advance, such as when the appointment is scheduled, or the process is automated, then it should be possible for each staff member in the front office to register 100 to 130 patients per day (see Exhibit 3.3).

The workload range depends on the number of new patients and the extent of additional assigned responsibilities, as well as the patient population, information system, level of automation, and other work processes at the practice. The more information you gather and/or deliver during the registration process (thus, the higher the transaction time), the lower the productivity you should expect.

Communicating the patient's arrival

After you have registered the patient, you must inform the clinical staff about the patient's arrival. Of course, they typically aren't at the desk next to you, but rather in another part of the office, busy with another patient. You certainly don't have time to leave the front office to track them down to tell them about every patient's arrival. Fortunately, this process — often referred to as the "arrival" process — has been thought through in much detail. A number of procedures and products are available to help you communicate efficiently and effectively with the clinical staff.

Here are common methods of communicating the patient's arrival:

- ➤ **Line of sight.** After the patient is processed, place the chart where the clinical team can see it. Charts can be stacked in a rack organized by physician, or simply on a ledge or counter. Use a convex mirror to "see" the charts around the corner.

- ➤ **Light system.** Press a switch at the reception desk to turn on a light at the nurses' station. Practices with several physicians use lights of different colors or lights that have flashing patterns.

- ➤ **Buzzers or chimes.** These can work through the telephone system or an intercom.

- ➤ **Charge ticket.** Print the patient's charge ticket to a printer situated at the nurses' station.

- ➤ **Pagers, radios, or other wireless devices.** Call or text the clinical staff's pagers, cellular phones, or other cordless devices.

- ➤ **Messaging systems.** Send an e-mail or instant message to the clinical team. (Be sure to follow security practices, because these systems can be used safely, but only when they are used correctly.)

- ➤ **Information system.** When registration is complete, send an automatic alert through the practice management or electronic health record system to indicate the patient's "arrival."

Each practice has its own requirements for handling the arrival process. Everything from insurance rules to technology to the amount of physical space your practice has influences how patients are processed through the arrival system. What's important is that you aren't the cause of a "lost" patient: learn your practice's arrival system and diligently perform it for every patient.

Conclusion

There are many factors related to the efficiency of the registration process that you can't control. At the same time, you can take steps to improve registration speed and accuracy. Alert your supervisor to the resources you need to perform your job effectively, improve your multi-tasking skills, and become knowledgeable in performing each task.

CHAPTER 3 QUIZ

True or False

Circle the correct answer.

1. Unlike many other businesses, medical practices cannot offer instantaneous check-in service because they must first gather the patient's name, insurance coverage, and other important details. **T   F**

2. A medical practice must never inform patients how much they are expected to pay on the day of their appointment. **T   F**

3. New patients take longer to register than patients who have been to the practice previously. **T   F**

4. New patients should be asked to show an insurance card and identification. **T   F**

5. Obtaining correct and complete information at registration is just a formality and has no impact on successful billing of insurance claims. **T   F**

Multiple Choice

Choose the one correct answer to each question.

1. Information that a medical practice needs from patients in order to register them includes:
   a. Contact information
   b. Insurance coverage
   c. Necessary insurance authorizations for certain services
   d. All of the above

2. Many of the steps of pre-registration can be done:
   a. Over the telephone
   b. Via the practice's secure patient Internet portal
   c. At a kiosk in the reception area
   d. All of the above

3. The encounter form, also called the superbill, is used by:
   a. Physicians to record services they perform
   b. Auto insurance companies to record accidents
   c. Customs inspectors at seaports
   d. None of the above

4. Industry averages indicate that registering a patient takes:
   a. 25 minutes
   b. 5 to 8 minutes
   c. Is not necessary
   d. None of the above

5. Common methods for front office staff to communicate the patient's arrival to the clinical staff include:
   a. A light system
   b. Buzzers or chimes
   c. Pagers or other wireless devices
   d. All of the above

Matching

Enter the letter of the correct definition from the right column next to the term in the left column that is the best match.

1. __ Assignment of Benefits

2. __ Notice of privacy release (HIPAA policy)

3. __ Financial policy

4. __ Medical records release

5. __ Pre-authorization

6. __ Non-Covered Services

a. Insurance company authorizes that it will pay for a certain service or procedure.

b. The patient agrees to permit the practice to release medical records on his or her behalf to third parties.

c. Used when the patient is to receive services that the physician knows will not be covered by the patient's insurance.

d. Form patients sign to show they understand and agree with the practice's billing and payment policies.

e. Form patients sign to assign their insurance benefits to the medical practice.

f. Form patients sign to acknowledge that they have been informed of the practice's HIPAA policies.

Answers to this quiz are in Appendix B.

CHAPTER 4

Telephones:
Techniques to Manage Calls

Introduction

What's your worst telephone experience? Was it calling the cable company? Or was it trying to find the right department at City Hall? For
some people, it is calling their medical practice.

Consumers give low ratings to the telephone service they receive at
many organizations, large or small. The problems seem to break down
into two categories: hard-to-use telephone systems and poor manners of the customer service representatives. Medical practices have an
opportunity to improve in both areas. As a staff member, you may not
be able to change how your practice manages telephone calls, but you
can do a lot to improve the system it already has. You can learn how
to use the telephone system more efficiently and display good telephone manners.

In this chapter, we review all aspects of the telephone. We look at the
types of telephone systems and how to use them. We also explain how
the customer service techniques discussed in Chapter 1, Customer
Service, also apply to the telephone.

The basics

The telephone is the front door to your medical practice — it's how most patients first come in contact with you and your fellow team members. These connections are often made when patients want to schedule appointments or find out more about the practice. Telephone contacts are the mode by which most patients gather their initial impressions of your practice, and first impressions count.

As the first person to answer the practice's telephone calls, you have a lot of control — more than you may think. If you are cheerful, responsive, and willing to help solve problems, patients get a positive impression of you and the entire medical practice. Having a strong desire to provide good customer service makes you more effective with callers and, in the long run, impresses the people that your practice values most: its patients.

It's not just initial contacts from new patients that count. Most of the connections that current patients have with your practice are not in person during office visits, they are over the telephone. Patients call to schedule appointments, renew their prescriptions, ask questions about their health, or inquire about their billing statements. In most medical practices, the front office team must answer these calls, forward calls to the right person on staff, and take effective messages.

Proper telephone protocol and manners should be second nature in this connected society. Unfortunately, people — whether employees of a cable company, the Department of Motor Vehicles, maybe even your practice — learn bad habits. Most people with poor telephone manners don't even realize that they are giving out a negative impression. This can make overcoming those habits and replacing them with new ones quite challenging.

We first discussed the importance of making a good impression on patients in Chapter 1, Customer Service. Now, let's learn how these concepts apply to specific tasks, including putting callers on hold, transferring calls, and taking messages.

Consistent greeting

Be prepared to answer the telephone. Answering the telephone is not an interruption; it's your job. Focus your attention on the caller.

Answer the telephone with a greeting that includes four important pieces of information:

1. Greeting;
2. Name of your practice;
3. Your name; and
4. A question asking what the patient needs.

Here is an example of all four elements at work: "Hello. Neurology Associates. This is Kelly speaking. How may I help you?"

Answering quickly

You never know when calls will come in. Doing your other work must, in many cases, be structured around meeting your practice's goals for telephone service. Answer all calls within three rings. Meet an average speed to answer 80 percent of calls within 30 seconds. Establishing standards for response time equates to meeting your callers' expectations of efficient service.

With a goal of answering all incoming calls within three rings, you may have to put some callers on hold to meet this expectation. If you do, be sure to get right back to the first caller. Don't leave callers on hold for more than one minute without checking back with them.

SCRIPTS SAVE TIME — GET RESULTS

Greeting callers

"Hello. Cardiology Consultants. This is John speaking. How may I help you?"

The art of putting callers on hold

There is clearly an art to putting a caller on hold. Rapidly saying "hold please" and quickly punching the hold button won't win you any awards. Callers don't want to be put on hold, so try to avoid it if you can. But sometimes it's necessary. Here's how to do it correctly:

1. Greet the patient just as you would any other telephone call: "Hello. Urology Associates. This is Julie speaking. How may I help you?"

2. Wait for a pause in the conversation. Apologize and explain the reason for putting him or her on hold: "Ms. Jones, I'm sorry that we are experiencing high call volume." Ask the caller's permission, and tell him or her that you will return to the call in one minute: "Ms. Jones, may I put you on hold for one minute, please?"

3. Wait for the patient's reply. (Usually he or she will say "yes.")

4. Check back with the caller if more than a minute goes by. Apologize for the inconvenience or thank the caller: "Ms. Jones, I'm so sorry that I had to put you on hold. Thank you for waiting. How may I help you?"

5. If applicable, tell the patient that you are still helping another caller. Ask if he or she wants to continue to hold or leave a message. *Never* make a caller call you back. If the patient can't hold any longer, then take the caller's number and call him or her back: "Ms. Jones, I am helping another caller. Would you

like to continue to hold, or is there a number for you so that I can call you right back?"

6. When you place a caller on hold to locate someone but that staff member has not yet picked up the telephone, say: "I'm still trying to locate Sally for you."

7. After you've paged a fellow employee, do not just leave the caller on hold indefinitely. Ask the caller if he or she wants to continue to hold or leave a message: "I'm sorry but Sally is not available right now. May I take a message and telephone number for her to call you back?"

Although callers don't want to be placed on hold, sometimes it's unavoidable. If you handle the situation professionally, you can turn a potentially frustrating event into one that leaves a positive impression on the patient.

 WORDS OF WISDOM

When a caller requests to speak with someone specific, avoid these responses:

➤ He's too busy.
➤ She isn't in yet.
➤ He went to get some coffee.
➤ She's gone for the day.
➤ I don't know where he is.
➤ She's in the bathroom.
➤ He took the day off.
➤ She doesn't want to be disturbed.

Instead, always use this statement:

> "He [or she] is not available at this time, Ms. Jones. Is there anything that I can help you with?"

BEST PRACTICES

Encourage your practice to program your telephone system to state informational messages about your practice, deliver health tips, and/or play music while callers are on hold.

Transferring calls

There is an art to transferring calls. This is not a reference to which buttons to push but, rather, how to handle the interaction. Before you transfer any call, listen carefully to what the caller says.

Listening means "not interrupting." Many times, it is immediately obvious what the caller wants and that you need to transfer the call to somebody else. It's tempting to interrupt, but don't. Hear the caller out. Interrupting is perceived as rude. If callers are upset about something, they think you are cutting them short. There's a very practical reason to listen to callers carefully: getting more detail about their issues could change the way you handle the call. The call you thought needed to be transferred to the business office, for example, might actually be a medical question for the telephone triage nurse, or vice versa.

Here's how an effective transfer should transpire:

1. Greet the patient: "Hello. Children's Medical Group. This is Leslie speaking. How may I help you?"

2. If the call needs to be transferred, tell the caller why you want to transfer him or her: "Ms. Jones, Eloise at our practice services desk can help you with your question about the referral."

3. Ask the caller's permission: "Ms. Jones, may I transfer your call to Eloise?"

4. Wait for the caller's reply. (He or she almost always say "yes.")

5. Tell the caller the name and number of the person to whom the call is being transferred: "Ms. Jones, it's a pleasure to transfer your call to Eloise at extension 76, who can help you with your question."

6. When connecting, stay on the line (if your telephone system allows it) long enough to ensure that the caller is being helped. Give the caller's name to the person to whom the call is being transferred. When appropriate, explain the nature of the call. "Eloise, I have Ms. Jones on the line. She has a question about her son's referral."

7. If the person is not available, offer to take a message or transfer the caller to voice mail. Don't just dump the caller into someone else's voice mailbox without any warning. "Ms. Jones, would you like for me to take a message, or would you prefer to leave a message on Eloise's voice mail?"

8. If the patient knows the party to whom they want to speak, transfer the call. "Ms. Jones, it would be a pleasure to transfer you to Eloise."

Make it a habit to follow professional telephone etiquette when transferring calls. Perceptions of rudeness and mistakes (such as hang-ups or being transferred to the wrong department) make callers irate.

Transferring calls on the telephone at work is part and parcel of any business, and it greatly affects how outsiders perceive your practice. A polite and smooth transfer tells callers your practice is a professional operation that knows what it is doing. Mishandling a simple telephone transfer can leave a negative impression — some people take it personally; others view it as incompetence. The fact that your telephone system might be hard to operate really doesn't make a difference to people who get cut off. Therefore, it's important to learn your practice's telephone system and — always — practice good etiquette when making call transfers.

SCRIPTS SAVE TIME — GET RESULTS

How to transfer a call

The patient's call needs to be transferred.

"It's a pleasure to transfer you to the business office. Here is the direct number in case the connection is lost: 111-222-3333."

Transfer the patient's call, and wait until the call has been connected before you hang up the telephone.

Transferred call is not connected, and the person or department you are trying to reach does not answer:

I'm sorry, but Susan is not available now. May I take a message, or would you like to leave a message on her voice mail?"

Take the message or transfer the caller to the voice mailbox as he or she requests.

- -

Handling the chatty caller

Some callers have a hard time getting to the point, so help them along by politely asking during a natural break in the conversation, "Ms. Jones, what can I help you with?" Practice with other staff in role-playing, such as during a staff meeting, to brush up on skills that help patients get to the point without sounding pushy.

Here's a tip to end a call with overly talkative people without hurting their feelings: wait for them to pause and then say, "Well, I won't take any more of your time...", or "Thanks for taking the time to discuss this. I know you must be busy, so...." Will this work? Usually, but not always. Some people are talkers. If the gentle approach isn't working, you may have to say, "Excuse me but I have calls from other patients coming in now. I'd be happy to call you back at a later time to help you."

Effective closing

Always, always let the caller hang up before you do. Close each call by thanking the caller for choosing your practice: "Thank you for choosing Neurology Associates for your medical care." If you work in a practice that treats children, your statement should be: "Thank you for choosing Pediatric Gastroenterology for your child's medical care." Regardless of the nature of the call, every caller should be thanked for contacting your practice. Showing appreciation at the end of the call is a great way to acknowledge that the patient had a choice to come to you.

 SCRIPTS SAVE TIME — GET RESULTS

How to close a call

Closing for all callers:

"Is there anything else I can assist you with?"

If the caller responds "no," use one of the following closings, depending on the relationship:

➤ If caller is the patient, say:

"Thank you for choosing Dermatology Associates for your medical care."

➤ If caller is the patient's parent, say:

"Thank you for choosing Dermatology Associates for your child's medical care." [Replace "your child's" with the appropriate relationship, or simply use the patient's name.]

➤ If the caller is not a patient, say:

"Thank you for calling Dermatology Associates."

Taking messages

Taking a good message is another skill that is often overlooked. You can set the stage by having the proper tools at hand. First, make sure your computer is always ready with an open Microsoft® Word document, a note-taking program, the task management module of your electronic health record system, or whatever messaging system your practice uses. Alternately, make sure there is pen and paper near every telephone. (If you take messages on paper, use a two-ply form to retain a copy of each message for liability purposes.)

Although things may get hectic at the front office, it's important that every telephone message contain the essential information the physician has asked for, such as the name of the caller (and name of the patient, if different), a patient identifier (for example, date of birth), date and time note is taken, reason for the call, and the patient's telephone numbers (at a minimum, capture a home and a cellular number; see Exhibit 4.1).

Getting the information in messages

Capturing complete and accurate information from every caller is essential to effective message-taking. If you fail to get the information, it's likely the patient can't be helped. If a patient asks to renew a prescription, for example, you need to know more than the patient's name and the medication. It's also important to get his or her physician's name, as well as the name and telephone number of their pharmacy. Based on each type of call, discuss with your supervisor what information you need to record.

When taking a message, it is important to focus on the following tasks:

> ➤ **Listen.** This means not interrupting the caller in mid-sentence to double-check information; instead, wait until

[EXHIBIT 4.1]   Sample telephone message template

Telephone Message

Caller's name:

Patient's name (if different):

Patient's date of birth:

Patient's account number:

Physician's name:
❏ Dr. Jones   ❏ Dr. Smith   ❏ Dr. White

Telephone numbers (best to reach; get at least 2)

(1)   (2)

Message:

Staff's name:

Pharmacy's name and telephone number (if applicable):

Forwarded to for resolution:

Date and time:

there is a natural break point and ask in a pleasant tone, "Ms. Jones, will you repeat that, please?"

➤ **Pre-empt.** Respond to patients who ask to speak with physicians or providers by asking if there is something you can do to assist the patient: "Is there something I can help you with today, Ms. Jones?" The patient may just need to schedule an appointment.

- ➤ **Complete.** Make sure to ask the patient for the information the physicians and providers say they need. If necessary, pull the patient's chart and attach the message to it.

- ➤ **Repeat.** Determine the accuracy of each message by reading it back to the caller.

- ➤ **Verify.** Look up the patient's account before the caller hangs up to make sure the patient is in the system.

- ➤ **Source.** Unless your system automatically stamps an identity date and time on the message, you should always include your initials on the message.

- ➤ **Deliver promptly.** Use an electronic messaging system that instantly transmits the message to the responsible party; ensure that paper messages are delivered without delay.

- ➤ **Resolve.** Keep messages on active status until the issue is resolved. Don't delete the electronic message or file it in the patient's record (or elsewhere if about a non-medical issue) until the matter is resolved.

Regardless of the nature of the message, try to capture *two* call-back numbers to reach the patient.

Handling questions

As a member of the front office, you recognize that you weren't hired to answer patients' medical questions. Even so, some patients who call have medical needs that should not wait for an appointment several weeks out. For those situations, you need to rely on your training, common sense, and, most importantly, the instructions of your practice's physicians.

You also should know which medical complaints could be a potential medical emergency. Your practice's physicians probably have developed protocols (definitions or brief descriptions) to guide you. For example, if a patient calls the office saying he is having trouble breathing, your physicians would want you to instruct him to call 9-1-1 immediately.

There may be other situations that require an urgent response. The medical specialty of your practice brings in different types of calls.

You should never give medical advice to a patient. Instead, ask the patient if you can transfer him or her to a member of the clinical staff.

The most important guideline to remember is: if you don't know, don't guess. Ask.

SCRIPTS SAVE TIME — GET RESULTS

How to handle a medical emergency

Patient is having an emergency (for example, difficulty breathing, uncontrolled bleeding, or chest pains).

"Please hang up and call 9-1-1. Are you able to do that?"

Make sure the patient understands you and do not keep him or her on the telephone.

Review your practice's protocol — your physicians may also want you to get the patient's name so one of the clinical staff can check up on him or her later. Do not depend on "caller ID" because it often does not detect wireless telephone numbers or the patient may be calling from someone else's wireless or land-line telephone.

Your goal is to get any patients who are having a medical emergency to promptly call 9-1-1 for help. You do NOT want to stay on the telephone with them any longer than necessary.

Your tone counts

In addition to *what* you say to callers over the telephone, recognize the impact of *how* you say it. Tone of voice is critical to successfully handling each telephone call. Answering the telephone is different than greeting a customer face to face. When you greet someone face to face, you notice their body language, make eye contact, and feel the energy. When you answer the telephone, the energy and excitement must be created. The way to generate that is with your tone. Tips for success include the following:

- End all conversations before you pick up the line.
- Speak clearly and distinctly in a pleasant tone of voice.
- Be direct, enthusiastic, and speak with a strong voice.
- Be calm, cheerful, and organized.
- Be prompt; pull up your messaging system and the patient's account as you answer the telephone.
- Don't chew gum or eat food.
- Avoid using a speaker telephone.
- Don't talk to others when you are on the telephone.
- Eliminate background noise, such as music or conversations between other employees.
- Speak at a normal pace so callers can always understand you (they may have a bad connection, be a little hard of hearing, or English might be their second language). Speaking rapidly makes callers think you are in a rush and want to get off the telephone — that might be true, but you are the practice's spokesperson during telephone calls and patients want to think that their medical practice has time for their concerns. Of course, speaking really slowly can cause the caller to think you are tired, sleepy, and likely to forget what they said.

➤ Talk directly into the mouthpiece. If this is a problem because you use other equipment while on the telephone (for example, a computer), consider asking your supervisor about purchasing a headset, which will free your hands.

Exhibiting a pleasant tone is essential to maintain a certain level of professionalism. Use your voice to leave callers with a favorable impression of you — and your practice.

BEST PRACTICES

How do you sound?

Because it's hard for us to "hear" our own voices, try recording yourself while answering phones. This exercise should only be performed in a medical practice with a supervisor's involvement. It could be done in a reenactment (at a meeting or training session) with other staff playing the role of the patient, or it could be done with "real" telephone calls.

(Supervisors conducting this type of training with actual patient calls should record only the staff member's end of the conversations, unless callers are informed about the recording, if dictated by state law. The recordings should be treated as sensitive information: don't make copies, don't let the recordings leave the practice, and erase all recordings when the exercise is complete, unless the recordings are used for an alternate purpose. Discuss this beforehand with your legal advisor.)

If you listen to a tape of yourself talking on the telephone at work or a similar situation, you may be in for a revelation. Do you have a calm and helpful tone of voice or do you sound like you are in a rush?

Five measurable standards of telephone service

Every time you pick up the telephone, you send an impression of your medical practice to the caller. They can't see through the telephone into your office, so sound and imagination form the impression. A negative impression could result in losing the caller to another medical practice.

Here are five telephone measurable service standards that many medical practices set for customer service. See if they are standards you can meet too.

1. **Response within three rings.** Although not all calls can be answered on the first ring, you should answer the telephone within three rings. An alternate measure is average speed to answer 80 percent of calls within 30 seconds. This may require you to put some callers on hold, and if so, first ask that caller for permission to be placed on hold.

2. **Short hold times.** At maximum, callers should not be placed on hold for more than two minutes in total, and no more than one minute without being spoken to.

3. **Quick messaging of patient medical questions.** Get any medical questions or related messages from callers to your clinical staff as fast as reasonably possible. URAC, a national health care accreditation agency, has established standards for response times for telephone-based nurse triage: the URAC Healthcare Call Center (HCC) Standard #13 requires a nurse to respond to a message from a patient within 30 minutes.[1] Even if your practice is not URAC accredited, it's still a good standard to meet. In addition to clinical or health questions, your practice should establish standard turnaround times for returning calls about prescriptions, billing-related questions, and referrals.

---

1. Bonnie Sturges, RN, Nurse Accreditation Reviewer, URAC, www.urac.org

You can help meet that standard by taking accurate and complete messages and then relaying them quickly to a nurse, physician, or other clinical staff as required.

4. **Minimum abandonment rate of five percent.** When a caller hangs up without getting through to a live person or gets tired of being on hold and hangs up, it's called "call abandonment." The percentage of calls abandoned should never exceed five percent. Your role is to handle telephone duties efficiently and try to get to every new call within the first three rings — keep in mind that the callers getting through to you might have already waded through a long menu of prompts ("press 1 to renew a prescription, press 2 to speak to a nurse...," and so on).

5. **Voice mail.** If your practice uses voice mail, pay close attention to your assignments to monitor and respond to voice mails. Typical voice mail expectations for office staff include:

➤ Consistent, pleasant greeting;

➤ Checking all voice mailboxes, at minimum, every hour;

➤ Resolving (bringing to a supervisor's attention, perhaps) any outstanding voice mail not handled by the end of the day; and

➤ Making sure callbacks have been performed and documented by the end of each day.

Some aspects of your telephone service, such as your tone of voice, are subjective, that is, a little hard to measure. But other things you do to handle telephone calls can be measured. These measurements might be part of how your job performance is evaluated (see Exhibit 4.2).

[EXHIBIT 4.2]			**Checklist for better telephone service**

Here's a checklist that supervisors use to assess their staff who answer telephones. Use it to see how you are doing.

Yes	No	Unknown	
			Answering time. Are telephones consistently answered on or before the third ring?
			Greeting. Is an appropriate and consistent greeting offered to all callers?
			Identification. Does the receptionist identify the practice and him- or herself?
			Query. Does the receptionist ask each caller how he or she can help them?
			Tone. Is the receptionist's tone of voice pleasant?
			Personalization. Does the receptionist use the caller's title and last name (for example, Mr. Jones or Mrs. Smith) whenever possible in the conversation?
			Recording. Does the receptionist record the information using a standard message-taking paper or electronic form?
			Clarity. Does the receptionist ask questions to ensure he or she understands the caller's question and verify with the caller by repeating or asking appropriate questions?
			Expectations. Are callers told when to expect a return call?
			Completion. Does the receptionist wait until the caller puts down the receiver?
			Comprehensiveness. Are complete messages taken consistently?
			Additional information. Does the receptionist gather other information needed to accompany the message (such as the patient's account number; pharmacy telephone number; etc.)?
			Accountability. Are messages initialed to identify who took them and are they delivered soon after being taken?
			Delivered. Are messages delivered to the appropriate party according to practice expectations?

Lessons from the pros

Why do some people have a knack for handling even the toughest, most complicated telephone calls from patients? Here are lessons from these telephone service pros.

Be happy (or at least act happy). You can sense someone's attitude by the tone of their voice. Patients hear it in your voice if you are smiling as you speak into the telephone. Try putting a mirror next to your telephone and smiling sincerely as you answer calls, just as you would do in a face-to-face encounter. The result is a more pleasing tone of voice — one that may help to soothe irritated callers (and you'll be able to keep an eye on what's happening behind you!).

Know your stuff. Patients call for so many reasons that locating the correct person on staff to answer a question can be a chore. Make a list of everyone's whereabouts — it can change daily (see Exhibit 4.3). Such a list saves precious time in looking for people and it lessens the callers' time on hold. There also are many common questions each day, so use scripted responses to get right to the point. Directions to the office, as well as places to which you commonly refer patients, should always be handy. If you can anticipate some of those questions, post them with the correct responses on your practice's Website in a "frequently asked questions" section.

Some people have a natural gift for handling telephone inquiries. Listen to how they do it, and use their skills to improve your telephone efficiency and service quality.

Training tips to improve telephone manners

The volume of incoming calls to a medical practice can be demanding — sometimes, overwhelming — but that's not a reason to give poor telephone service. Appropriate telephone call handling is a key part of your practice's service to its patients.

[EXHIBIT 4.3]   Daily locator list

	MON	TUES	WED	THURS	FRI
Dr. Apple	rounds: 7–9 a.m. clinic: 9:30–11:30 a.m. lunch: 11:30 a.m.–12:30 p.m. clinic: 1–4 p.m.	Off	rounds: 7–9 a.m. clinic: 9:30 a.m.–5 p.m.	Off	rounds: 7–9 a.m. clinic: 9:30 a.m.–11:30 off: 11:30 a.m.
Dr. White	clinic: 8 a.m.–12 p.m. lunch: 12–1 p.m. Crosstown Day Surgery: 1–5 p.m.	rounds: 7–9 a.m. clinic: 9:30–11:30 a.m. lunch: 11:30 a.m.–12:30 p.m. clinic: 1–4 p.m.	Crosstown Day Surgery, 8 a.m.–12 noon lunch: 12 noon–1:00 p.m. office work: 1–5 p.m.	rounds: 7 to 9 a.m. clinic: 9:30–11:30 lunch: 11:30–12:30 clinic: 1–4 p.m.	clinic: 9 a.m.–12 noon off: 1 p.m.
Nurse Jones	walk-in/urgent: 8–10 a.m. injections & misc: 10 a.m.–12 noon lunch: 12 noon–1:00 p.m. lab & office: 1–4 p.m.	walk-in/urgent: 8–10 a.m. injections & misc: 10 a.m.–12 noon lunch: 12 noon–1:00 p.m. lab & office: 1–4 p.m.	walk-in/urgent: 8–10 a.m. injections & misc: 10 a.m.–12 noon lunch: 12 noon–1:00 p.m. lab & office: 1–4 p.m.	walk-in/urgent: 8–10 a.m. injections & misc: 10 a.m.–12 noon lunch: 12 noon–1:00 p.m. lab & office: 1–4 p.m.	walk-in/urgent: 8–10 a.m. injections & misc: 10 a.m.–12 noon lunch: 12 noon–1:00 p.m. lab & office: 1–4 p.m.

Be prepared. Keep a pen and writing tablets near all phones. Turn on the computer at your workstation as soon as you get to work. Even though your practice may use computer entry to record notes of patient calls, it's still wise to also have a pad of paper handy for those times when the computer screen freezes up or other technical problems happen.

Get the name...and keep it. Make a note of the caller's first and last name as soon as the caller states it. If the caller starts the conversation without giving a name, ask for it at the first opportunity by saying, "May I ask who's calling, please?" If necessary, confirm the spelling. Writing down the name at the beginning of the conversation is critical to a good telephone exchange. Some patient's questions get very involved. You may forget the person's name as you listen to the details of his or her request, which forces you to ask for the name again at the end of the conversation. Then the caller may wonder what other information you missed. After you have the name, use it often during the conversation. The name offers a connection to the patient, and demonstrates that you are listening and attentive.

Use a consistent greeting. Use your practice's full name, or the name that your supervisor suggests. Even if it is a long name, and you are saying it 50 times a day, you must remember that each caller is hearing it just once. Say the name and greeting statement clearly, with expression, and do not rush through it. Your supervisor may have a preferred greeting; always use it so there is consistency in how patients are greeted on the telephone.

Avoid verbal abbreviations. It may be quicker to say, "Hello. Gyne Onc" (as opposed to "Hello. Gynecologic Oncology Associates"), but you'll lose time in the long run as callers pause and wonder if they reached the right place. Everyone who answers the telephone should say your practice's name with as few abbreviations as possible. It makes a more professional impression and ultimately contributes to a higher level of service.

Watch non-verbals. A bad mood or lousy attitude seems to leap through the telephone. Watch inadvertent non-verbal communications, such as sighs or moans. Beware of talking too rapidly or loudly as well as using a condescending or inappropriate tone. Make a point of smiling as you speak — patients sense that smile, even over the telephone.

Maintain a calm demeanor. If the caller has a complaint about your practice or is simply taking out their bad mood on you, don't absorb their emotions. One defense against absorbing a caller's "bad vibe" is to post an inspiring quote, happy photo, or artwork on your workstation that can be a source of calm. It can give you something to focus on when difficult situations arise.

Prepare for rough spots. Script a few phrases for lead-in statements in difficult situations, such as a customer who is complaining. For example: "I'm sorry that we didn't meet your expectations, Ms. Jones." Try to remain diplomatic and polite; getting upset only makes the caller angrier. Always show willingness to resolve the problem or conflict. Write down the caller's comments and verbally summarize the complaint at the end of the conversation. Your summary will indicate that you took the complaint seriously. Many callers just want to be heard.

Before the telephone call ends, be sure to tell the caller clearly the next step that you will take with the question, comment, or complaint. This action might be to give a note to the physician or nurse, ask someone from a department to call the patient, and so on. Also give the patient a realistic estimate of the time it will take to get a response, using the response time for callbacks agreed upon by your practice and approved by your supervisor (for example, three hours).

Know how to say "no." Many times you will not be able to fulfill the patient's request while on the telephone: the person to whom they want to speak isn't available, the results of a lab test are not yet available, or they want something that is not in line with your practice's protocols. Learn the techniques of saying "no" in a way positive way. It may sound like a contradiction, but there is a big difference between saying, "No, we can't do that" and "Let's see what we can do."

Conclude calls with a bang. Use the patient's name — "Ms. Jones," "Mr. Smith," for example — at the end of conversations. Stating the patient's name tells the patient that the problem is being handled by you — one of their physician's competent staff. Thank the patient for choosing the practice, particularly if the person is scheduling an appointment. Wrap up calls by asking the caller if there is anything else they need. For example: "Thank you for choosing the Cardiovascular Surgery Group, Ms. Jones. Is there anything else I can do to assist you?" If performed consistently, you leave a positive and memorable impression on every caller (see Exhibit 4.4).

BEST PRACTICES

Handling difficult patients on the telephone

➤ Demonstrate warmth and individualized attention by using the patient's name frequently and by listening.

➤ Use a sincere voice; it has a calming effect on the caller.

➤ Listen completely to the complaint, allowing the caller to vent.

➤ Acknowledge and show appreciation for patients' feelings and their right to feel that way.

➤ Demonstrate willingness to resolve the problem.

➤ Never deny, belittle, or dismiss what the caller is saying.

➤ Avoid being defensive.

➤ Focus on solving the problem rather than internalizing the caller's attacks.

➤ Don't place blame; apologize: "I'm sorry that this happened..."

➤ Alert your supervisor to disgruntled and hostile patients.

Proper business telephone etiquette requires that you help the
caller feel better emotionally, as well as address the nature of their
call. When you solve both challenges at once, you create a positive
opportunity for you and your practice.

[EXHIBIT 4.4]	Create a memorable — not a miserable — impression
DON'T say:	**Instead, DO say:**
Who is this?	May I have your name, please? *or* With whom am I speaking?
Hang on.	May I please put you on hold?
Please hold.	May I please put you on hold? *(Then wait for a response.)*
Transferring you now…	Thank you for calling. I would like to transfer you to someone in our Referrals Department who can assist you. In case our connection is lost, here is the direct telephone number of the Department: *[insert telephone number]*. It's a pleasure to transfer you now.
What's your name? What's your date of birth?	May I have your name, please? May I have your date of birth in order to verify our records?
Who's your doctor?	In order to best serve you, could you please tell me the name of your physician?
I don't know.	That's a good question. Let me check and find out. *or* I don't have the answer right now. I will get back to you within the next 15 minutes. Will that be acceptable? I am sorry for the inconvenience. What is your telephone number?
We can't do that.	That's a great question. Let's see what we can do. *(Then find an alternative solution.)*
No one can help you.	I'm sorry, but no one in our business office is available right now. Would you like to leave a message on the voice mail *[if available]*, or may I take a message for you?

[EXHIBIT 4.4]	(continued)
DON'T say:	**Instead, DO say:**
No one can help you.	I'm sorry, but no one in our business office is available right now. Would you like to leave a message on the voice mail *[if available]*, or may I take a message for you?
No…	We will be able to have the results by noon tomorrow. Where can we reach you?
What do you want?	Is there something that I may help you with?
Just a second.	It may take me 2 to 3 minutes. Are you able to hold while I check?
You'll have to…	Here's how we can help you with that…
Are you serious? (Referring to a complaint.)	Thank you for bringing that to our attention.
No one here would have promised you anything like that.	If I understand you correctly, you were promised… Let's figure out how we can resolve this.
He doesn't want to be disturbed.	He is out of the office. Can someone else help you or would you like for me to take a message?
She's at lunch.	I'm sorry, but she is not available. May I have her call you later or can someone else help you now?
She is in the bathroom.	I'm sorry, but she is not available. May I have her call you later or can someone else help you now?
He's too busy right now.	He is unavailable. May I be of assistance?

Refer callers to your Website

You may find yourself spending a lot of time on the telephone with new patients. They often have questions about the insurance you accept, billing processes, practice hours, the location of the office, driving directions, parking, and more.

Of course, you should answer the patient's questions as you are able, but you can reduce callbacks by suggesting that patients visit your Website or Web-based portal if they need more information.

Many practices try to reduce the volume of incoming calls by putting the following information and tools for patients on their Websites or portals:

> **Appointment scheduling.** Patients can request appointments or schedule directly online.

> **Test results.** With the patient's permission, test results can be posted for patients to access securely.

> **Prescriptions.** Patients can request prescription renewals and authorizations.

> **Forms.** Registration and medical history forms can be downloaded by patients.

> **Referrals.** Patients can request referrals and receive confirmations.

> **Visits.** Patients can request an online visit, and receive medical care via a secure part of the Website or portal.

 FYI

The right way to refer patients to your Website

A patient calls and asks for a medical records release form. How do you respond?

   A.   "It's on our Website."

   B.   "It's on the home page of our Website. I'd be happy to e-mail the link or fax the form to you."

Answer: B. When patients have a question or request, try to help them — really help them — and give them options. It's the little things that count.

If your practice's Website or portal displays the hours of operation, financial policies, locations, directions, services, and so forth, then patients can find this information and won't need to call you to get it.

Telephone systems: What you need to know

A telephone system can involve complex technology. You must master your duties with this system to make the patient's experience positive — and your supervisor and physicians happy. Get to know your telephone system by understanding how the following processes function.

Auto attendant. System that answers and routes calls after prompting callers. It allows callers to select option by using their telephone's keypad. For example, "Hello, you've reached Family Practice of Anytown. If you know your party's extension, please dial it now. Please dial 1 for appointments, 2 for the nurse, 3 for prescriptions, and 4 for billing and referrals. Dial 0 or hold for the operator."

Automatic call distributor (ACD). Software products that help telephone operators better manage incoming calls by distributing calls evenly to staff, pointing callers to specific functions (appointments, prescriptions, etc.), and placing callers on automatic hold — "in queue" — until a staff member is available to take the call. ACDs can be used in place of or as a backup to a receptionist.

Call accounting. Software programs that capture, record, analyze, and organize call data. The information is stored in a database that can be queried for operator productivity, call abandonment rate, and other analyses.

Call forwarding. Allows you to program the system to ring elsewhere if a station is busy or a call is not answered within a predetermined number of rings. Some systems permit external forwarding; some forward only within the system.

Call hunt. Bounces incoming calls automatically to the next available (not busy) line.

Call park. Allows you to place callers "in orbit," removing them from general telephone traffic in order to alert employees that a call is waiting.

Call transfer. Allows calls received from internal or external callers to be sent from one telephone to any other within the system.

Caller identification (ID). Allows you to identify the caller's registered name and number. On an outbound basis, it allows a caller to identify your practice. Some practices "block" their caller ID to help protect their patient's confidentiality — blocking prevents other members of the household or friends from seeing your practice's name on the patient's caller ID display or log of received telephone calls.

Capacity. The number of telephones, lines, and software that a telephone system can handle. For example, a 24-port system can handle a combination of 24 lines and telephones.

Central processing unit (CPU). The main cabinet that houses the system's intelligence and controls its activities.

Custom call routing (CCR). Enables you to design custom routing points for callers — a big plus offered by some auto attendants. For example, a caller can leave a message in a mailbox and then be routed to specific locations within a practice.

Direct inward dialing (DID). Enables a caller to bypass the receptionist and go directly to the desired extension. DID trunks are assigned through the telephone company. Each trunk ordered has 24 associated telephones, each of which can be assigned to individual staff.

Interactive voice recognition (IVR). Software that prompts callers for information by asking them to use their telephone keypads or, in some systems, utter certain phrases in response to automated questions. IVR improves staff efficiency by routing callers to the appropriate staff based on information the caller provides.

Intercom. Enables you to ring another telephone within the system and talk internally without tying up an outside line.

Predictive dialer. A computerized system that automatically dials batches of telephone numbers for connection to staff. These systems adjust the calling process to the number of staff members it anticipates (or predicts) will be available when the calls being placed are expected to be answered. The predictive dialer discards unanswered calls, engaged numbers, disconnected lines, answers from fax machines, answering machines, and similar automated services and only connects staff to the calls that are actually answered by people.

Voice over Internet Protocol (VoIP). Technology that enables routing of voice conversations over the Internet or any other IP network; also referred to as IP telephony and Internet telephony. The voice data flows over a general purpose, packet-switched network instead of the traditional dedicated, circuit-switched voice transmission lines.

Don't let the complexity of a telephone system ruin your interaction with callers — be sure to pay careful attention during your training session with your practice's system, as every system works a bit differently. Today's technology allows you to handle more calls than ever before. But when call management skills are lacking, the only thing you get from all that technology is the ability to serve more patients poorly.

Preventing telephone systems from compromising patient confidentiality

HIPAA — the federal Health Insurance Portability and Accountability Act — requires that a "reasonable" effort be made to protect patient health information. The law is aimed at protecting the patient's medical and personal information. Even before this law was passed, medical ethics set the precedent of respecting patient confidentiality and privacy. Here are ways that your practice can live up to this ethical duty.

Policies and procedures. Telephone policies should be based on sound business practices, common sense, and the use and disclosure of the minimum protected health information required to perform the specific task.

Position of operators. If you're answering the telephone, it's best to be located away from an area where patients could overhear private information. This isn't always possible, especially when you must greet patients as they arrive and also answer telephone calls. Use your best judgment: do not, for example, read back their social security or credit card number, and try to use only their title and last name (Mr. Jones, instead of Robert Jones). Discuss with your supervisor about how to best preserve patient confidentiality — and get your job done.

Blocking caller ID. If your practice provides services that may be considered sensitive (the specialties of psychiatry, obstetrics, and infectious disease are a few that come to mind), it may block its caller ID when calling patients about an appointment or report that a test result has arrived. This blocking prevents your practice's name and number from appearing on the caller ID display on the patient's telephone. Sometimes this is done only for patients who request it. Some patients do not want others in the patient's household or business to know about their medical care.

Custom telephone greeting. Some practices instruct staff to answer phones with the names of the physicians instead of the name of the specialty or full name of the practice. For example, instead of saying, "Infectious Disease Consultants" in your telephone greeting, you might answer, "Drs. White and Smith." This protects your patients' confidentiality in the case of curious family members, friends, or coworkers of the patient who might redial your number from the caller ID or a telephone's memory.

Reminder calls. Your "Notice of Privacy Practices," a requirement of HIPAA, should include a statement that you may place appointment confirmation calls. Consider including a consent form for these calls in new patient registration materials. If a patient declines to allow you to make any reminders by telephone, respect this request. If patients agree to allow reminder messages to be left on their voice mail or answering machines, make sure you know what information is to be included. HIPAA rules instruct medical practices to limit information to the minimum necessary, but they do not specify what should be included or excluded. Industry practice has been to limit the information to patient's name, date, time, and physician's last name. An example is: "This message is for Jane Doe. You have an appointment with Dr. Jones on Tuesday at 2 p.m." Do not include the specialty of your practice or the nature of the appointment. If your reminders are communicated through the mail, e-mail, or texting, use these same guidelines about the patients' permission and offer only minimal information.

Patient preference. Some patients want more confidentiality than others. They may want to keep all of their medical affairs hidden from their family members, coworkers, and friends. This may affect how — or whether — you leave appointment confirmations and other messages on their voice mail. Asking patients the best way to handle communication to them from your practice should be part of the new patient registration procedure. It's a good idea to get these preferences in writing so it can be easily seen in their medical chart.

Discuss with your supervisor about observing these requests. Patients lose a great deal of trust in your practice if you do not respect their wishes for privacy.

Conclusion

Good telephone etiquette has a real business purpose: it makes patients feel respected, cared for, and confident that they are working with a professional medical practice.

From the patient's point of view, the difference between a good and a bad experience when calling your practice is *you*. You provide the human "touch" in communications to patients when they call. Your telephone manners and efficiency give callers a feel for what it is like to be a patient at your practice. Use every moment on the telephone with each patient as an opportunity to build a relationship with your medical practice.

CHAPTER 4 QUIZ

True or False

Circle the correct answer.

1. Consumers tend to give low ratings to telephone service because of the poor manners of customer service representatives. **T   F**

2. Most of the contacts that current patients have with their medical practice take place via e-mail. **T   F**

3. It's always a good practice to ask the caller's permission before transferring them into a voice mailbox. **T   F**

4. Medical practices allow front office staff to give medical advice to patients on issues if it's something they know about from personal experience. **T   F**

5. Front office staff who are assigned to check the practice's voice mail are usually required to check it at least once an hour. **T   F**

Multiple Choice

Choose the one correct answer to each question.

1. The four elements of an effective greeting to patients who call the practice include:
   a. Name of your practice
   b. Your (the operator's) name
   c. Asking patient what they need
   d. All of the above

2. The number of rings it takes front office staff to answer telephone calls is important because it is a good indicator of:
   a. Customer satisfaction effort by staff
   b. Electricity use
   c. How many telephone extensions are working
   d. None of the above

3. Besides the patient's name, important information to get when taking a message from a patient is:
   a. Physician name
   b. Identifier(s) such as date of birth
   c. Two telephone numbers (at least one)
   d. All of the above

4. The percentage of abandoned calls (when callers hang up because they are tired of waiting) should never exceed:
   a. 1 percent
   b. 5 percent
   c. 15 percent
   d. 25 percent

5. The tool known as the daily locator list is important for receptionists and others working in the front office because it helps them to locate _____ at any hour of the day:
   a. Supplies
   b. Vendors
   c. Physicians, nurses, and other clinical staff
   d. Patients' closest relatives

6. Good tips to handle patients who complain include:
   a. Counter every point they make with a good defensive argument
   b. Be very casual
   c. Use the patient's name frequently to show attention
   d. Don't bother your supervisor when upset or hostile patients call

Matching

Enter the letter of the correct definition from the right column next to the term in the left column that is the best match.

1. __ Telephone scripts
2. __ Acronym/Verbal abbreviation
3. __ Direct inward dialing (DID)
4. __ Call hunt
5. __ Non-verbals
6. __ Auto attendant
7. __ Notice of Privacy Practices release

a. Unspoken communications detected over the telephone.
b. A patient consent form required by HIPAA.
c. Allows callers to select options using their telephone keypad.
d. Written statements for telephone operators to use.
e. Shortening the practice's official name (to be avoided when answering telephones).
f. Bounces incoming calls to next available (not busy) line.
g. Enables callers to bypass receptionist and reach an extension.

Answers to this quiz are in Appendix B.

CHAPTER 5

Scheduling:
Setting Appointments for Patients

Have you ever thought about how the airlines make money? The key is to fill up the plane — to make the most of the salaries, gas, supplies, and other overhead being spent on every flight. You may be wondering why we're talking about airplanes when this book is about medical practices. There's striking similarity between an airplane taking off and the beginning of a day in a medical practice.

Like the airplane, it's the practice's goal to make the most of the overhead it spends: salaries, supplies, and so on. The most significant trait that airlines and medical practices share has to do with their customers — passengers can't be added once the plane takes off and patients can't be added once the day is done.

A physician's time is much like an airplane's capacity: each appointment slot is a seat on the physician's plane. Filling every seat means improving the bottom line — and getting patients to their destination — a healthy tomorrow. It's your job to make sure that the seats are full.

A medical practice lives by its daily schedule.

In this chapter, we examine the basic scheduling methodologies, best practices in scheduling patients, and how to handle emergencies, cancellations, no-shows, and other events that can disrupt the daily schedule.

Scheduling: The basic methodologies

To start, let's get the basic scheduling methodologies down. Your practice likely uses one of these approaches. We also look at the pluses and minuses of each form of scheduling so you can anticipate them, and we suggest some steps you can take to make each form run smoother.

Medical practices use three general methods of scheduling: single interval, multiple interval, and block (or wave) intervals.

- **Single intervals.** Each visit receives the same amount of time on the scheduling calendar, regardless of the patient's status with your practice (new or established) or the patient's chief complaint (health check or problem-focused visit). An example is scheduling all appointments on the quarter hour.
  - *Pluses:* Simple to schedule; eliminates any guesswork.
  - *Minuses:* Some patients may need more time, others less. Single-interval scheduling can translate into lengthy patient waits.
  - *Making it work:* Practices that use single-interval scheduling choose a time interval for appointments that is as close as possible to their average patient encounter (10 minutes, 15 minutes, etc.).
- **Multiple intervals.** In this approach, the intervals between appointments depend on the nature of the visit. For example, a patient needing to see the physician for a sore throat (a "problem-focused visit with a single complaint") would get a 15-minute slot on the scheduling calendar, but a new patient needing a full exam would be given 30 minutes.
  - *Pluses:* Maintains a lot of the simplicity of the single-interval system but also allows for some variations. The multiple-interval schedule helps avoid long patient waiting times.

- *Minuses:* You must know how to give the appropriate appointment slots. Some patients want to come in for problems that don't neatly fit the scheduling slots. For example, the patient with the sore throat might also have diabetes that's been hard to control.

- *Making it work:* Practices using multiple intervals try to keep it simple with no more than four or five appointment types. It's also important that you are trained to identify the patients who are most appropriate for the available time slots. The process works best when you are knowledgeable about your specialty, and physicians or nurses review each upcoming day's appointment schedule to spot any potential problems. Sometimes it is possible to double-book a time slot when the physician or nurse is certain, for example, that a patient won't take that long.

➤ **Block (wave) intervals.** This approach just gives several patients a single block of time. You do not have to consider the type of visit or the patient's chief complaint. For example, all 12 morning appointments are asked to present at 9 a.m. and are seen in some predetermined order until the end of that morning's clinic.

  - *Pluses:* The physician's time is always optimized because there is no waiting for a late arrival or standing around because of a patient who misses his or her appointment.

  - *Minuses:* Most patients have to wait — and wait a long time.

  - *Making it work:* Many medical practices modify the block/wave approach by scheduling patients in smaller blocks of time, such as every 30 minutes. This reduces patient waiting times but also helps keep the physician's time optimized because there's less chance he or she will wait idly when some patients arrive late — or not at all.

Making it work

The time assigned to each appointment depends on your practice, and perhaps even your physician. Follow the protocols developed by your practice about how to schedule, but seek clarification if you need it. Scheduling can be tricky if you work for a multi-specialty practice because there are so many different types of patient complaints. The physicians or clinical nurse supervisor may develop a list of questions for each specialty to help you establish the appropriate amount of time needed for various types of patients.

Scheduling the appointment

When a patient first calls for an appointment, that's your chance to introduce your practice — and make the best impression. Take the initiative to:

- ➤ Greet the patient and state your name.
- ➤ Ask how you can help the patient.
- ➤ Ask the patients who are interested in being seen which physician (or provider) they wish to see.
- ➤ Determine why they are calling to schedule an appointment (often referred to internally as the "chief complaint").
- ➤ Query as to what date and time would accommodate the patient. Offer another physician if the patient's needs are urgent and the physician being requested is booked or out of the office. (Some practice's have nurse practitioners, physician assistants, or other clinicians who can see patients too.)
- ➤ Based on the patient's requests — and your ability to meet them — propose an appointment day of the week, date, and time to the patient.
- ➤ If it's acceptable, repeat the time and date.

➤ Confirm insurance and demographic information for established patients. For new patients, capture all information in accordance with the protocols established by your business office manager. (See Chapter 6, Time-of-Service Payments, for more information about the insurance verification process.)

➤ Ask the patient for his or her preferred contact point, as well as cellular phone number. (The information is important for your practice's contingency plan to contact patients if the physician must tend to an emergency, communicate a test result after the appointment, and so forth).

➤ Ask the patient from where or whom he or she was referred.

➤ Describe the practice's policy regarding patient payments at the time of service.

➤ Advise the patient of any outstanding balances, and (if possible) offer to collect the amount by credit card over the telephone.

➤ Remind the patient of information that they need to bring with them, as well as any fasting, dietary, or other preparations needed for the visit.

➤ Repeat the information about the appointment, including day of week, month and day, and time.

➤ Conclude the call by thanking the patient for choosing your practice.

➤ Wait until the patient disconnects before you hang up the telephone.

As a member of the scheduling staff, you are the practice's greeter, sales representative, and reservation agent — all in one.

See the Sample Scheduling Script on page 96 for ideas on how to plan your scheduling calls.

More scheduling tactics that please patients

There are more ways that medical practices make the scheduling process run smoother while keeping patients happy. Determining which of these tactics to use is a matter of policy that is up to your physicians and supervisor to decide.

Ask patients whether your practice can e-mail appointment confirmations or text the reminder to their cellular phone. Unless there are extenuating circumstances, the patient should confirm this request in writing. (Note: Do not send patients reminders via Twitter, postings on their personal Facebook page, or communications about appointments through other types of social networking.) Just as in a telephone reminder, never reveal the details of the patient's visit in an e-mail or text message.

Direct the patients to learn more about your practice, including directions and registration forms, by visiting your practice's Website or Web-based patient portal. Ideally, if your practice posts its registration forms for patients to download, ask them to complete the forms first and bring them to their visit. Some medical practices have a secure sign-on process where patients can safely complete and transmit their registration information online.

Indicate any preparations the patient needs to make. For example, some patients may have to fast before they give blood for a test. You might have to remind others to bring radiologic films or current medications with them. Your supervisor should provide you with written instructions — often organized by medical complaint — to remind you which patients should get these instructions.

Facilitate any additional visits that may be prompted by the appointment you have scheduled. This is an "add-on" appointment that would be indicated for you by a nurse or your supervisor. For example, your practice's physician may want a patient to go to the lab before being seen at your practice. If so, it's important that you pass along those instructions to the patient or proceed with scheduling both appointments; otherwise, the physician will not have necessary information at the time of the visit and both the patient's and the physician's time will be wasted.

Use the rotation list. Practices with more than one physician often set up a rotation list for front office team members to use when patients call for an appointment but don't have a specific physician they wish to see. Using these rotation lists is easy: as new patients call in, give Dr. Jones the first patient, Dr. Smith the next, Dr. White the next, and then repeat. Using the rotation list correctly is important because getting new patients is critical for the physician to maintain a viable practice.

 FYI

Watch that rotation

You wield a lot of power in making sure that new patients who don't have a physician preference are equitably distributed to the practice's physicians. Sometimes it may be tempting to steer more patients to one physician over another because, well, some physicians are more pleasant to work with than others or perhaps a physician has directly made the request to do so. Be careful about playing favorites. Denying a physician an equal chance to get new patients can hurt the physician's income and possibly overburden the other physicians.

Exceptions: Sometimes you may be instructed to intentionally steer new, unassigned patients to one physician. This often happens when there is a new physician in the practice who needs to build a clientele.

Never decline to recommend. Some patients who are unassigned to a physician may ask your opinion. Don't say "I can't recommend anyone." That sounds like you *don't* recommend anyone. And saying "I'm not allowed to recommend anyone" sounds just as bad. Instead, suggest that the patient visit your practice's Website to read more about each of the physicians. For example, respond to the requests by saying: "I highly recommend visiting our Website and going to the 'About Our Doctors' link to learn about the expertise, education, and experience of each of our providers." If the patient continues to press you for a recommendation, pass them along to your supervisor by saying, "I'd be happy to have our office manager contact you directly." Note that some practices, particularly primary care practices, offer "get-to-know-you" visits, tours of the practice, and/or other types of introductory sessions for new patients. If your practice offers those services, be sure and suggest them to the patient who is undecided.

These tactics and others your practice uses makes for a smooth scheduling process that both pleases patients and allows for efficient use of the physician's and clinical staff's time.

SCRIPTS SAVE TIME — GET RESULTS

Sample scheduling script

"Hello. Practice Associates of Anytown. This is Elizabeth speaking. How may I help you?"

Patient asks to schedule an appointment.

"Certainly, may I have your name please?"

Patient provides name.

"Ms. Smith, is there a particular physician who you'd like to see?

Patient responds with "Dr. Jones."

"Is there a date and time that would work best for you?"

Patient suggests next Wednesday after 2 p.m.

"Ms. Smith, Dr. Jones doesn't have any appointments available next Wednesday afternoon, but he does have an open appointment time the following day, Thursday, November 5, at 2 p.m. Would that work for you?"

Patient responds that next Wednesday is necessary.

"Ms. Smith, Dr. Jones' partner, Dr. Walker, is available next Wednesday at 2 p.m. May I schedule that appointment for you?"

Patient responds in the positive.

"Ms. Smith, for our records, what is your current address?"

Patient responds.

"What is your current insurance coverage?"

Patient responds.

"Is there someone who we may thank for referring you to us?"

Patient responds.

"Is there a telephone number that we may use to best reach you?"

Patient responds.

"Do you have a cellular phone number where you also wish to be reached?"

Patient responds.

"Ms. Smith, we have you scheduled for Dr. Walker, next Wednesday, November 4, at 2 p.m. Payment is expected at the time of service. Thank you for choosing Practice Associates of Anytown."

Wait until the patient hangs up before you release the call.

For specialty practices handling referrals

When a patient is referred to your practice, the initial contact for scheduling the first appointment may be the patient, but it also may be a staff member from another practice who schedules the appointment on behalf of the patient. Either way, make the best of these contacts to obtain needed information. This communication is an opportunity to gather some necessary information before the patient presents to your practice for the appointment.

How much information is reasonable to gather from a referring practice if its staff schedules a new patient? Generally, you should be able to very quickly obtain the patient's name; home, work and cellular phone numbers; the chief complaint and diagnosis(es); the insurance company; and a referral number if the insurance company requires it. (See Chapter 3, Registration, for more information about the registration process.)

Many practices now speed up this process by providing referring physicians access to a referral management function on a Web-based patient portal. This allows referring physicians to alert you of their request to refer a patient to your physician. It may be your job to check these incoming scheduling requests. You may be the person they call when the online scheduling tool doesn't work for them. You also may be the person who checks the fax machine and e-mail box for incoming information about these referred patients, or the one who has to call back the referring practice when information is incomplete. To lessen the likelihood of a missed appointment, contact the patient directly to confirm the appointment time and date.

Emergencies

Some patients may call your practice when they are having a medical emergency. If your practice uses an automated telephone attendant (see Chapter 4, Telephones), the recorded greeting should always tell patients experiencing emergencies to hang up and call 9-1-1.

All the same, a few patients having medical emergencies may still try to get through to you first. Chapter 4, Telephones, explains what to do when this happens; namely, instruct the patient to hang up and then dial 9-1-1 or proceed directly to the emergency room. If you give these instructions, make a note afterward of the conversation you have with the patient, including the particulars about the date and time. Pass this information on to your supervisor immediately. Don't keep the patient on the telephone trying to obtain their insurance company, plan number, and other data. In medical emergencies, seconds count.

When delays happen

Emergencies that delay physicians occur from time to time, and there are effective ways to handle these unexpected delays. When an emergency arises and a physician can't see scheduled patients on time, you will have tasks related to managing the patients who are currently in the practice and waiting — see Chapter 7, Waiting — but you likely will have some additional scheduling duties too.

When the information about the wait is communicated to you, ask your supervisor about the options for handling the impacted patients:

> Can you overbook that afternoon's clinic?
> Will the physician be able to see the delayed patients through his or her lunch hour or after hours?
> Are other physicians in the practice going to work in any of the delayed patients?

Be sure to seek guidance from the physician's clinical support staff if there is a patient scheduled for an acute problem who will be affected by the delay. You don't want to reschedule that sick or ailing person for the next available appointment if it's four weeks out. In some cases, making them wait even four more days might not be well received.

The length of the delay will help you decide whether you should tell patients about the delay at all. For example, a five- or ten-minute delay probably won't wreck the whole day's schedule, but an hour's delay would call for immediate action. In Chapter 7, Waiting, see the section, "Managing unpredictable delays" for the techniques in giving information about delays to the patients who are already waiting.

Informing patients. Without revealing any details of the emergency, inform patients who are waiting that there will be a delay. For delays that could be more than an hour, you should also get on the telephone and start contacting the patients with appointments later in the day.

When you inform patients of a delay, don't just say, "The doctor is late." You'll get no sympathy — and frustration levels will still run high. Give the patients a message that says the physician is indeed doing something very important, but stop short of giving any details. It helps patients put their feelings of being inconvenienced into perspective. For example, say: "Dr. Smith was called to the hospital for a patient who's been in a serious accident." If you don't know any details at all, at least give an explanation that indicates the physician is helping another patient. For example, "Dr. Smith was unexpectedly called to attend to a patient who's having an emergency."

Don't try and guess at the time of the delay. The clinical staff will likely inform you if they know about the delay, so if you know how long it will be, tell the waiting patients what to expect. If you don't know, be honest about it.

Handling long delays. If there is going to be a significant delay, it may well become a scheduling issue. Give patients the choice of:

➤ Rescheduling for another day (or whenever the physician says he or she will be available);

➤ Seeing another provider (if this option is available); or

➤ Waiting.

There will be some patients who your clinical staff does not want you to reschedule. These will likely be those with important problems that shouldn't be handled at a future date. A good message to give these patients is: "Dr. Jones wanted me to let you know that he is truly sorry about the delay, but he would appreciate your waiting." Depending on the time involved, you can advise the patient to leave and return at a later time — or reveal that you can call or text them when the physician has returned to the office.

Advising patients who have not yet arrived. After giving information about the delay to the affected patients who've already arrived, get on the telephone to make the same offer(s) — reschedule for another day, see a different provider, or come in and wait — to the patients who are scheduled for appointments later in the day. (This is where a cellular phone number can come in handy!)

This extra communication and rescheduling can take time. Depending on how many patients are involved, you may need to ask another staff member to come to the front office to help you. If you are working elsewhere in the office, be prepared to help out with rescheduling tasks when delays occur.

Appointment confirmations

There are many ways that medical practices handle appointment confirmations. Although a few still choose not to remind patients of upcoming appointments, most practices recognize that a missed appointment means lost income. Plus, a lot of preparation goes into every patient appointment; if the patient never shows, that's wasted time and money. Some practices use the 15-minute rule when they can't confirm every appointment; that is, they only call the patients who may need longer than 15 minutes with the physician. Another guideline might be to only give reminders to those who are receiving services that require special equipment, medication, or preparation.

Here are the do's and don'ts that medical practices follow in deciding how — and when — to confirm appointments. Review them to learn some of the reasons behind your practice's appointment confirmation procedures.

➤ Don't say "remind." Some people may infer that you don't trust them to remember. So instead, say that you are calling to "confirm" their appointment — it makes patients feel like they are in control.

➤ Include enough details. You'd be surprised at how little patients might remember about their appointments. When confirming an appointment, it's important to include the physician's name (but *not* the specialty), day of the week, the date (month and day), time, location (unless you only have one), *and* your telephone number.

➤ Leave good messages. Speak clearly, not too fast, and in a pleasant tone of voice.

➤ Repeat the telephone number twice and not too quickly — rattling off a string of seven or, in many areas, 10 digits quickly at the very end of the message may require the patient to listen to the whole message over again (many people do not know how to "rewind" their voice mail so they end up listening to the entire confirmation again).

➤ Do not make calls more than 72 hours in advance of the appointment, unless you have the resources to make multiple calls. People are more likely to forget something that is several days in the future. Calling two days in advance allows the patient enough time to cancel or reschedule 24 hours before the appointment.

➤ For long appointments, ask the patient to call your practice back to confirm.

➤ Maintain a "priority" list — a waiting list — for patients who want to be seen earlier (see the "Using the priority list" section on page 104). As you make confirmation calls, some patients may ask to be rescheduled. Subsequently pull patients from the priority list to fill those now-empty slots. Of course, don't forget to cancel the originally scheduled appointment for the patient on the priority list who gets moved up.

➤ Never leave a message on voice mail that mentions the nature of the patient's visit or includes your practice's specialty. Other people may have access to that message, which could compromise the patient's privacy.

➤ Be ready to supplement automated confirmation calls with "warm" calls. Some practices assign a staff member to personally place a telephone call to a subset of their patients, such as those who are scheduled for lengthy appointments, new patients, or those who have missed their appointments in the past.

➤ Send an e-mail or text message. More practices are sending appointment confirmations via their Web-based patient portal, or by e-mail or text message. If this is your assignment, be sure to avoid communicating the specialty or the reason for the appointment in the communication to the patient.

Confirming appointments isn't just a way to get patients in the door, it's an important step in an efficiently run medical practice: it ensures that patients know when to arrive and what preparations, forms, documents, or payment are needed.

An effective appointment confirmation process is critical to avoid the problems — and costs — associated with missed appointments.

SCRIPTS SAVE TIME — GET RESULTS

Sample appointment confirmation script

"Good Morning. This is Betty calling to confirm your appointment with Dr. White on Tuesday, June 8, at 9:15 a.m. If you have any questions or need to reschedule, please call our office at 123.245.7890."

Using the priority list

Maintain a waiting list — but call it a "priority list" to ensure that patients know they're your priority — for patients who ask to be seen sooner than the next available appointment. A priority list helps fill appointment slots that are open due to late cancellations, and it improves customer service. This list should include patients' names, contact information (two telephone numbers are ideal), and account numbers. There also should be columns for the date the patient was placed on the list and the date of their original appointment (the one they don't want to wait for). Put an "X" in that column if they have no appointment scheduled and just want to get in at the first opportunity. It's also a good idea to have a "Notes" field on these lists. Make a note in it when you try to contact a patient but cannot reach them. Your practice likely has a policy on how to leave messages on a patient's voice mail, so be sure to abide by that. Alternatively, your practice may also have a policy about whether you should give priority list patients that you miss on the telephone a chance to call back. Many practices find it much simpler to just move down the list until they reach a live person on the other end of the telephone and confirm that he or she will take the open slot.

Using the list is pretty simple: as soon as you are advised of a cancellation, either by the patient or another staff member, call the first name on the list.

The best place to store this list is in a spreadsheet file on your practice's internal network. That way, you or anyone else in the practice can quickly access the list. If your practice doesn't have such a network, then the list should be maintained on the computer of the staff member who handles most of the scheduling duties — likely, that's you. With the list on a network or a workstation computer, your team members won't have to interrupt you or hunt around the office for a sheet of paper that could be on a desk somewhere just to add a name.

When the appointment for a priority list patient is scheduled, you can cross out his or her name. It's a good idea to purge the list weekly. In a weekly purge, highlight the names of all patients who are accommodated and be sure to close the loop by releasing those patients' originally scheduled appointments.

The priority list is an easy way to convert cancelled appointments into revenue-producing visits, but it also does something else. The very fact that you keep a priority list garners a positive reaction from patients.

Cancellations

Cancellations come in two forms: the ones given several days in advance and the ones that come with very little notice. Cancellations made on the same day are likely to create holes in the schedule that you must scramble to fill. The difference between cancellations and no-shows is that the patient who calls to cancel — even at the last minute — is at least attempting to be considerate. It also allows you the opportunity to fill that appointment slot with another patient. A last-minute cancellation means you won't have time to schedule another patient. If the cancellation comes in at the last minute, the time you and other staff spent preparing for that cancelled patient — pulling and previewing their chart, verifying their insurance, and perhaps stocking special supplies — is now wasted.

Track cancellations. If your practice is having problems with last-minute cancellations, it may decide to track and analyze them. Your attention to detail in helping to do this tracking will provide important information to your supervisor and the practice's physicians. Tracking cancellations over time can show certain patterns such as:

- Cancellations seem to always come in for Monday morning appointments or just after a three-day weekend;
- One physician or one satellite office gets the most cancellations; or
- Cancellations tend to come from patients in a certain age group or with a particular type of insurance.

Understanding these patterns helps your physicians and supervisor decide when it's safe to double-book a provider or how to structure staff workloads. Cancellation patterns can also point to problems in the practice's relationship with its patients.

Prevent cancellations. Your practice should try to prevent cancellations whenever possible. You can do this by reminding patients of the practice's cancellation policy whenever they schedule appointments, when appointment confirmations are sent, or when patients ask to cancel on short notice.

Try to head off last-minute cancellations. Making confirmation calls 48 hours in advance can help. Another tactic some practices try is to tell patients that cancellations must be made no less than 24 hours in advance (or some other deadline) or there will be a financial penalty. If your practice has a penalty for last-minute or same-day cancellations, you should be sure to politely remind patients of these consequences when they call to make appointments.

A last-minute cancellation could be handled in the same way as a no-show with the same penalties. Penalties don't have to be in the form of a financial charge. Your practice may decide to not give repeat offenders the prime times for appointments, such as first thing in the morning. Instead, they might only be offered appointments at the end of the day, or perhaps even dismissed from the practice.

Some practices dismiss patients who make several last-minute cancellations or who skip several appointments. Dismissing a patient must be done carefully to avoid legal problems (such as being accused of abandoning the patient), so it would likely be handled by a physician and a supervisor, after discussions with your malpractice carrier.

Every once in a while, a patient has a legitimate emergency that requires canceling an appointment on short notice. We'd like to think that coming to see a physician is the most important thing in the patient's life, but there can be good reasons to cancel, such as car problems, a child's illness, an emergency at work, and so on. In your role as appointment scheduler, you may get these calls routed to you. Although a cancellation may cause more work for you and other staff, be careful not to alienate patients who are trying to be considerate.

Follow up on cancellations. Patients who cancel are sometimes making their last call to your practice. They cancel out of respect for your time but do not intend to return. They may have found another physician or they may not like the service they've been receiving at your practice. It's a wise idea to follow up with any patients who cancel but do not reschedule within five working days of the cancellation. Your supervisor may have set aside time in the day for you or someone else to call these patients and encourage them to schedule another appointment. Or at the very least, to hear why they are dissatisfied, record their concerns, and give the findings to your supervisor.

Make it convenient for patients to cancel. Putting the phones on hold at lunch makes it harder for patients to cancel. The lunch hour is a convenient time for many working people to make personal calls, such as to their physician. Making it hard for patients to cancel effectively increases your rate of missed appointments. Your practice may offer a cancellation voice mailbox as well as an e-mail address. If your assignment is to check the voice mail and e-mail boxes several times a day, be sure to attend to these duties in a timely manner. A patient who gets a response within one working day is more likely to reschedule the appointment.

 FYI

Cancellation trends

If your practice produces daily reports about appointments and cancellations, here's why. A medical practice's fill rate tells you how well the practice's cancellation policy works and how well you manage the "cancellation conversion" process. Cancellation conversion is turning appointment cancellations into patient encounters, instead of leaving them as empty (and non-reimbursed) slots on the daily schedule. To figure this rate, your practice compares the number of patients each provider can accommodate based on his or her appointment template with how many they actually saw. For example, if your practice had the capacity to see 60 patients last Wednesday but physicians and other clinical staff only saw 52, then your practice's fill rate was 87 percent (52 divided by 60). Ideally, the fill rate should be at or close to 100 percent. Anything less is "excess capacity." In addition to simply not having enough patients requesting appointments, there are other causes of excess capacity: patients who don't show up (no-shows), cancellations that are not converted into appoint-ments, or physicians who are not in the office because of emergen-cies. By analyzing the fill rate, your practice can spot opportunities to improve income.

Cancellations — even one that's early in the day — can disrupt work flow, raise stress levels, and potentially cost the practice money. Using the strategies described here, you can help your practice reduce, or even avoid, many of the problems caused by cancellations.

Physician cancellations

Sometimes physicians cancel their clinics because of a patient's medical emergency. In other cases, it is because the physician has personal business or takes a vacation. Many medical practices have policies to require physicians to schedule out-of-office days six to eight weeks in advance. When these cancellations happen with very little notice and scheduled patients are affected, they are called "physician bumps," meaning the physician has bumped his or her patients from the schedule that day.

At some practices, physicians never bump appointments. Others — perhaps yours — have a significant or developing problem with the issue. A physician's cancellation of an appointment can disrupt a patient's life in many ways: the patient has to rearrange time off work and potentially cause disruption to his or her coworkers. The patient may also have childcare issues, family activities, and any number of other obligations to rearrange. Most importantly, the patient's care may be negatively impacted.

If physicians are bumping patients too often, it can degrade your practice's reputation with patients. Patient complaints about being bumped can also get back to your referring physicians. Those physicians may start thinking twice about sending patients to your practice.

SCRIPTS SAVE TIME — GET RESULTS

The rescheduling call

Because being bumped by a physician is disruptive to the patient, it is important that you handle the rescheduling call carefully. One way is to develop a script for these calls.

"Ms. Smith, this is Gloria from Endocrinology Consultants. Dr. Jones asked me to contact you personally. There has been a change in her schedule that will impact your appointment. She asked that I contact you to tell you that…"

Go to option A or B:

Option A: *"… one of Dr. Jones' partners, Dr. Smith, will be seeing you on your appointment date. Dr. Jones wanted me to reassure you that she will review your care with Dr. Smith following her return. Do you have any questions about this change?"*

Respond to the patient's questions. If the patient has no questions, thank the patient for choosing Endocrinology Consultants and conclude the conversation.

Option B: *"… your appointment with her will need to be rescheduled. Do you have your calendar available?"*

Pause for the patient's response.

*"Thank you. The dates that Dr. Jones has available are …
Dr. Jones is very sorry that she inconvenienced you."*

Once the patient schedules the appointment, thank the patient for choosing Endocrinology Consultants and conclude the conversation.

Appointment recalls

Appointment recalls are how a practice tracks and encourages patients to be seen for a follow-up visit(s) or preventive care that the physician recommends. Sometimes the patient is asked to come back in a few weeks or months so the physician can check on something that came up during an office visit. Alternatively, the patient may have a medical condition that requires a status check annually or a few times a year. Finally, the patient may need preventive care based on his or her diagnosis, age, gender, or other factors, as recommended by the physician.

Follow-ups the old way. Here's how medical practices traditionally handled follow-up care appointments:

> ➤ Schedule an appointment based on the recommendation of the physician;

> ➤ Give the patient a card with the time and date written on it; and

> ➤ Assume the patient will show up several months later for the appointment.

For follow-up care that was recommended but not available in the practice, patients were typically told about the need for the subsequent care at their visit. Patients were then expected to make the appointment for the recommended care.

But, of course, issues arise in patients' lives. Conflicting things get scheduled: vacations, out-of-town business trips, and so on. But wait, you say, we have a scheduling system that is set up to make a reminder call a day or two before that appointment next year. Unfortunately, there's a good chance that six — or maybe even three — months down the road, the patient will have completely forgotten about that appointment and have a conflict, therefore needing to reschedule. The result is more work for you and more uncertainty about whether the practice can fill its appointment slots that particular day. Finally, if they never scheduled the appointment in the first place — with you or another provider — patients are not just inconveniencing the practice, they're not receiving the care they need.

Follow-up scheduling — new tactics. Developing a better recall system can be an effective alternative to give patients appointments in the distant future. When the physician asks a patient to return in 12 months, your practice may decide to record that request in a recall system but not make an actual appointment yet. When 10 months have passed, the recall system reminds *you* to communicate with the patient to schedule the appointment. The same system can be used for reminding patients of recommended preventive care, even if it's a reminder to seek care outside of your practice.

There are hosts of ways to recall patients for recommended medical care. Here are ways that practices schedule recall appointments.

- **Card system.** When a patient completes his or her visit, write out a card that records: (1) the recommended care and (2) the date in the future it is needed next. File the cards by date going up to 12 months into the future. Query the cards once weekly, contacting patients due for care in the following four to 13 weeks. If you have an electronic health record (EHR) system, this is likely an included, automated function.

- **Computer system.** Most practice management and EHR systems have built-in recall functions. The system's vendor can explain how these functions work.

- **Log.** Keep a log of patients who need follow-up care. Organize the entries by the month into the future that the patient will need to return. (Many EHRs have functions that make this easy and are integrated with the scheduling module.)

- **Envelopes.** Ask the patient to write his or her address on a blank envelope. File the envelope in a filing system organized by month. Go through the files weekly and mail envelopes, with a notice to contact your practice (or another provider) to schedule the recommended care, four to six weeks before the appointment is needed.

➤ **Calendar.** Develop a paper or electronic calendar to record recalls. If, for example, a patient visits on May 15 and needs to return for a regular quarterly follow-up visit in mid-August, record the patient's account number and a note on the calendar in mid-July so you know four weeks before the appointment to send a recall notice or place a telephone call to the patient. Follow that with a reminder telephone call one or two days prior to the day of the appointment.

➤ **Register.** Automated patient registries — standalone or built into an EHR or Web-based patient portal — allow you to monitor patients according to a pre-determined schedule of care. After you register the patient, the software alerts you to upcoming patient needs, such as a follow-up appointment, test, or visit to another provider. Send a secure message, write a letter, or call the patient to schedule the appointment.

A smooth functioning appointment recall process accomplishes two important goals for the medical practice: it helps patients stick with their physician's medical treatment plan, thus improving the quality of care you provide, and it reduces the chances of a no-show.

Scripts that improve the scheduling function

One place to use scripts is when handling scheduling appointments. A lot of information must be gathered in a short amount of time. These exchanges often take place on the telephone, so it is important to ask clear questions and make good notes of these conversations. Scheduling also is done as the patient is leaving the practice following an appointment. In both cases, there may be a tendency to rush the exchange of information. To reduce the chances of forgetting to ask for some key information, use a script that reminds you of the important questions to ask.

Scripting these encounters also helps you to deliver the right messages about what the patient needs to know about the appointment — and what you need to know for appointment scheduling.

Try modeling your own script (based on your practice's scheduling protocols) on the sample scripts used by medical practices provided in Appendix 5A.

Conclusion

Your scheduling responsibility helps the practice run efficiently. It also has a direct impact on the satisfaction of your practice's patients and referring physicians. Good organization and management of the appointment scheduling process contributes to a successful medical practice.

Appendix 5A: Scripts for Success

• •

Scheduling

Appointment request. The caller may be the patient, a family member of the patient, or the staff at another physician's office making an appointment so one of their patients can be seen by your physician. If the call is coming from outside, answer with your practice's standard greeting.

If... it is a transferred call, begin by saying:

> *"Hi, this is [your name]. I'd be happy to help schedule an appointment. Is the appointment for you or another person?"*

Uncertain appointment request. Sometimes it won't be clear to you whether the patient wants to schedule an appointment or has a question about something else. In those cases, say:

> *"Thank you for calling Practice Associates. Are you interested in scheduling an appointment with one of our physicians/providers?"*
> [Say *"providers"* if your practice also offers appointment with non-physician providers, such as physician assistants, nurse practitioners, midwives, audiologists, etc.]

If... the caller is NOT the patient:

> *"What is the patient's name?"*

If... the caller is the patient, prepare him or her to get insurance information:

> *"While we're setting up your appointment, could you please have your current health insurance card ready? I'll have some questions that need information from your card."*

If... the caller says "no," offer to wait while the patient retrieves it, to have the patient call back when he or she has it, or to call the patient back at an agreed time. Then say:

"This process will take a few minutes and then I can proceed with helping you to set up the appointment."

Then confirm that the patient is a new or existing patient:

"Have you been a patient here before?"

If... the caller is NOT the patient, replace "a patient" with the name of the patient. For example, if the mother is calling about her son, Johnny Smith, say:

"Has Johnny been a patient here before?"

If... yes, then ask:

"May I have your first and last name please?"

After getting the name, verify the spelling. Then call up the existing patient record in the information system to confirm the patient's demographic information and tell the patient:

"Mr./Ms._____, I am going to review some information with you to verify that our records are up to date."

Discuss with your supervisor which questions you should ask the patient from the following list to verify the record of an existing patient.

If... the patient is new to your practice, you need to gather additional information:

"I am going to ask you a few questions in order to set you up as a patient in our scheduling system."

Then ask:

"What is your mailing address?" [Verify street address, apartment number, city, state, and zip code.]

What is your date of birth?

What is your gender [if it's not obvious]?

"What telephone numbers may we use to communicate with you?"

If the patient asks why you need the telephone numbers, say:

"These are the telephone numbers we will use to make appointment confirmation calls and communicate with you about other items such as test results."

"What is your Social Security number?" Note: Ask only if your practice needs this number and be prepared to explain why.

"Were you referred to us by another physician?"

If another physician referred the patient, ask:

"May I have that physician's name so we can send him or her information about your visit?

Then ask the patient to verify the spelling of the referring physician's name. If the patient does not know how to spell the name, ask for the referring physician's specialty and record it in the Notes portion of the record.

Gather additional demographic information by asking the following questions:

*"What is the **name listed on your insurance card?**"*

*"What **insurance** plan card do you have?"*

*"What is the **subscriber number?**"*

*"What is the **member number?**"*

*"Do you have **other insurance?**"*

If the patient indicates that he or she does not have the time to provide the information now, offer the individual the option of calling back when it is more convenient or calling him or her back at an agreed time.

Collect the same information as above about the secondary insurance.

"Is this a work-related injury or illness?"

If the patient doesn't know but there is an indication that the illness or injury occurred at work, collect information about his or her employer just in case it is a work-related injury.

Information needed for a work-related injury includes:

➤ Accident date

➤ Number

➤ Employer

➤ Employer mailing address

➤ Employer city, state, zip

➤ Employer telephone number

Commence the scheduling portion of the call by asking:

"Is there a particular physician with whom you'd like the appointment?"

Allow the caller time to state a physician's name, if is or her so chooses, then pull up the schedule for that particular physician.

If... there is **no particular physician**, ask:

"Is there a particular date and time that you're looking for, or would you like our first available appointment?"

Allow the caller to respond to your question, then pull up the schedule based on his or her response. Then ask:

"What is the nature of your complaint?"

Allow the caller to describe the reason for the appointment. If **the patient is reticent**, say:

"Knowing the nature of the appointment will help us identify an appointment that allows the physician to have enough time to address your concern."

Schedule the appointment, saying:

"We have you scheduled for an appointment regarding (their stated complaint). *Is this correct?"*

If... the caller **offers additional complaints**, be sure to: (1) choose an appointment time that accommodates the individual's request or (2) indicate to the patient:

"We'd be happy to schedule another time to address that issue."

After you have settled on a mutually agreeable date and time, say:

"We have an appointment available on [day of week, month and date, time of day]. Does that work for your schedule?"

If... the caller indicates that it's not acceptable, try the next appointment slot, and repeat the process.

If... the caller indicates that the appointment is acceptable, say:

"Thank you. We have you scheduled for [day of week, month and date, time of day with Dr. XYZ]."

Insert any instructions or statements, such as:

"Please bring your referral with you."

"We'll call you two days before your appointment to confirm this time."

"Please do not eat or drink six hours prior to your appointment, with the exception of water."

End the call by saying:

"Thank you for choosing Practice Associates. We look forward to seeing you then. Is there anything else we can assist you with?"

Handling exceptional issues

If... the caller asks, "Is that **a student (or resident)?**" say:

"Our practice does participate in teaching. Every student [or resident] is paired with a faculty attending physician who will be managing your care."

If... the caller **asks for a specific physician** with whom there is **no appointment available**, say:

"Dr. [XYZ] does not have any appointments available at this time, but I can see if one of Dr. [XYZ's] partners has an appointment available or I can place you on our priority list for an earlier appointment that may come up in the event of a cancellation."

Then look up an appointment with another physician, Dr. [ABC] and say:

"We have an appointment available with Dr. [ABC] on [day of week, month and date, time of day]. Does that work for your schedule?"

If... the caller **indicates that it's not acceptable**, try the next appointment slot, and repeat the appointment statement.

If... the caller **indicates that it is acceptable**, say:

"Thank you. We have you scheduled for [day of week, month and date, time of day with Dr. ABC.]"

If... there is **no acceptable appointment slot**, put the patient on the priority list, according to the practice's protocols.

If... caller asks for the **cost of the appointment**, discuss your practice's policy about minimum time-of-service collections, to include any minimum deposit. If no payment is expected at the time of service, insert the range of the cost, such as "$100 to $500, depending on the services that your physician recommends."

If... the caller's insurer requires a **managed care referral**, say:

"Mr./Ms._____, your insurance plan requires you to obtain a referral from your primary care physician for this appointment. If you have not already done so, please contact your primary care physician's office to obtain this referral. If you have specific questions or need assistance with obtaining a referral, you may contact our business office at [phone number]."

If... your practice **does not participate** with the patient's insurance, say:

"Mr./Ms._____, please be aware that your health plan is not participating with the Practice Associates and may require you to pay a higher out-of-network coinsurance or may not cover the visit. If you have specific questions about your benefit plan, you should check with your health plan or your employer's human resources office directly. You can reach your health plan by calling the toll-free number on your insurance card."

CHAPTER 5 QUIZ

True or False

Circle the correct answer.

1. In single-interval scheduling, all appointments get the same amount of time on the scheduling calendar no matter what type of patient or type of visit it is. T   F

2. An appropriate greeting when patients call for an appointment is to state the name of the practice, your name, and to ask the patient how you can help. T   F

3. It is not recommended to send patients appointment confirmations via Twitter or posting on their personal Facebook (or similar) pages because those systems are not secure. T   F

4. Tracking the reasons patients give for cancelling appointments can uncover problems in the practice's relationship with its patients. T   F

5. Reminding patients of the practice's appointment cancellation policies is not considered much help in preventing cancellations on short notice. T   F

6. If physicians bump patients from appointment times too often, it can degrade your practice's reputation with patients. T   F

7. It's a safe bet to assume that patients generally won't need any help from the medical practice to remember a follow-up appointment that has been scheduled several months out. T   F

Multiple Choice

Choose the one correct answer to each question.

1. A big disadvantage to single-interval scheduling is:
   a. Staff doesn't know when the day starts
   b. Some patients may end up waiting a long time
   c. Patients forget to bring necessary documents
   d. All of the above

2. To make multiple-interval scheduling work, the medical practice must:
   a. Train scheduling staff to identify patients who are more appropriate for various time slots
   b. Have physicians or nurses review each upcoming day's schedule
   c. Keep selection of appointment types simple (4 or 5 types)
   d. All of the above

3. The reason given when a patient asks for an appointment is called the:
   a. Follow-up
   b. Chief complaint
   c. Authorization
   d. None of the above

4. A good place to direct patients to learn more about your practice (such as its physicians, directions to get there, forms, etc.) is:
   a. City Hall
   b. eBay
   c. Your practice's Website
   d. Your personal opinions

5. The priority list (also called a waiting list) is useful because it:
   a. Allows patients who need urgent visits to get in earlier
   b. Helps work in new patients who don't have a specific physician
   c. Helps reduce open slots caused by last-minute cancellations and no-shows
   d. All of the above

6. Scheduling options that can help handle a long delay when a physician is detained by a medical emergency are:
   a. Overbooking that afternoon's clinic
   b. The physician seeing patients through the lunch hour or after regular hours
   c. Other physicians in the practice work in the delayed physician's patients
   d. All of the above

7. Getting a second telephone number from a patient who schedules an appointment is a good idea so you can:
   a. Check on the patient's credit
   b. Increase your chances of reaching the patient
   c. Determine if his or her mailing address is correct after an appointment
   d. None of the above

Matching

Enter the letter of the correct definition from the right column next to the term in the left column that is the best match.

1. __ Single interval
2. __ Multiple interval
3. __ Block (wave) intervals
4. __ Rotation list
5. __ Priority list
6. __ No-shows
7. __ Chief complaint
8. __ Scripts
9. __ Referral
10. __ Appointment confirmation

a. Several patients are scheduled in a single block of time regardless of type of visit or chief complaint.

b. All visits get the same amount of time on the scheduling calendar, regardless of type, chief complaint, etc.

c. A list that helps staff assign physicians to patients calling in for the first time.

d. Reminding patients of an upcoming, scheduled medical appointment.

e. Patients who don't show for their appointments.

f. The reasons a patient gives for wanting to be seen by the physician.

g. Also known as a waiting list — for patients who want to come in earlier than what's open on the schedule.

h. Pre-written statements or notes that remind you what to say or ask when talking to a patient.

i. Appointment intervals differ based on type of visit, chief complaint, etc.

j. When one physician sends a patient to see another physician.

Answers to this quiz are in Appendix B.

[CHAPTER 6]

Time-of-Service Payments:
Collecting from Patients

As a consultant, I often speak to medical office managers and physicians who complain that their patients say they forgot their checkbook or didn't know their insurance company required a $40 copayment for every doctor's office visit. What I like to say in response is: "People don't go to McDonald's, order a meal, and tell the cashier, 'Oops, I forgot my wallet. Could you just bill me?'" Yet, that's what people have come to expect at their doctors' offices. Turning around these attitudes is our challenge.

Once upon a time, people with medical insurance could see their physician and not have to pay any cash at the visit. They expected their physician to bill their insurance first and then send an invoice for whatever they owed. Historically, the invoice was for a small portion of the bill, if anything at all. A lot of patients still expect this, even though most of us now have insurance plans that require time-of-service payments and significant out-of-pocket payments. And then there are the patients without any insurance coverage at all.

Things have changed. As a result, the staff at the front office of a medical practice plays a critical role in helping to collect money from patients. You are collectors.

This chapter discusses:

➞ Varying degrees of time-of-service financial responsibilities;

➞ The importance of insurance verification;

➤ Effective techniques to collect payments from patients; and

➤ Finalizing collections at check-out.

You play a critical role in ensuring that your practice optimizes its collections potential. Without you, the practice would have to pay for printing and mailing more patient statements, and your colleagues in the business office would have to make more collections calls. As a member of the front office team, you are at the forefront of collections — your efforts can enhance the practice's ability to collect payments and be successful.

 FYI

Terms that staff collecting payments must know

Accounts receivable. This is an accounting of the moneys owed but not yet collected from insurance companies and patients for services your physicians have provided. It can take a month or more for most claims to get paid, but the longer that unpaid claims sit in accounts receivable, the less value they have to your practice. Collecting time-of-service payments helps keep those amounts off the accounts-receivable ledger.

Allowable. This is the payment that your practice agrees to accept, by Current Procedural Terminology (CPT®) code, from an insurance company with which your practice participates (see "Participation"). In essence, it is a discounted price that your practice accepts as payment in full from participating insurance companies. The allowable is sometimes referred to as the "allowance."

Charge. The charge is your practice's fee for the physician's services. Your physicians establish a charge for every service they render. Each CPT code is assigned a charge amount. These charges are submitted to insurance companies or to self-paying patients. However, your practice agrees to accept a lower payment (the allowable) for services to patients covered by insurance companies with which your physicians participate. The difference

FYI (continued)

between the fee and the allowable is written off as a "contractual adjustment."

Coinsurance. Coinsurance is a form of cost sharing. After the patient's deductible has been met, the insurance company begins to pay a percentage of the patient's bills. The remaining amount, known as coinsurance, is the portion owed by the patient to your practice. For example, an insurance policy may cover 80 percent of the allowable, leaving the remaining 20 percent as the patient's financial responsibility.

Copayment/Copay. This is a payment established by the patient's health plan for a specific type of visit. This amount is due from the patient (or the patient's guarantor, such as a parent) at the time of service. This information can routinely be located on the patient's insurance card. There are different amounts according to the type of visit. You may see, for example: Emergency Room Visit — $100, Inpatient Stay — $200, Physician Office Visit — $40.

CPT. This is the acronym for Current Procedural Terminology, a system owned by the American Medical Association in which thousands of physician services are given individual codes. Physicians use these codes to describe the services they provide to patients when filing claims with insurance companies. The practice's superbill usually lists the most frequently used codes so physicians can easily check them off after providing services to patients.

Deductible. The deductible is an amount that must be paid on an annual basis before the patient's insurance company commences payment. This amount is established based on the patient's health plan, and it may vary based on the service. For example, there may be no deductible for preventive care (often referred to as "first dollar coverage"), but a deductible may apply for sick care. Deductibles are usually calculated on a calendar-year basis. They also can be based on the anniversary date of the patient's effective date with that plan or the anniversary date that the subscriber

FYI (continued)

joined the plan. An "unmet" deductible refers to the amount of the deductible that has not been reached. An "unmet" deductible is the patient's financial responsibility.

Denial. Health plans refuse to pay for a physician's service when they do not receive enough information to process the claim. This may be due to a mistake or omission by a member of the front office team, such as not getting the patient's name correct or their complete insurance identification number, and so forth. Denials cannot be charged to the patient. The practice must spend time and money to correct and resubmit that claim to the health plan if it wants to get paid.

Explanation of benefits (EOB). This is a notice a patient receives from his or her health plan after the claim for healthcare services has been processed. It explains the amounts billed by the practice, what the health plan paid, denied, discounted, or does not cover (non-covered service). It also lists the amount the patient owes your practice. In the event of a denial by the health plan, the EOB may also communicate information needed to process the claim.

Non-covered service. This is a service for which the insurance company will not pay, and for which the patient is responsible to pay.

Out-of-network. This refers to services rendered by a provider that does not have a contract with the patient's health plan. Typically, health plans contract with a panel or "network" of physicians, hospitals, and other health providers. If patients receive care outside of their health plan's network, then they may be financially responsible for some or all of the care provided.

Participation. When your physician signs a contract with a health plan to discount services to the plan's beneficiaries, your physician is considered a participating physician. The discount comes in the form of the allowable. Your physician also agrees to accept the health plan's administrative policies, procedures, and

FYI (continued)

requirements. Your physician can still treat patients of non-partici-
pating health plans, but those patients may have to pay more, and
your practice may have to bill them directly.

Payer. A third party — often an insurance company — that is
responsible for reimbursing the physician for services to the
insured patient, who is referred to as the "beneficiary." A payer
typically offers several health plans, each with a different benefit
and financial structure. In addition to government and private
payers, payers also include workers' compensation, employers, and
self-funded plans.

Superbill. This is an electronic or paper list of the most frequently
used CPT codes so physicians can easily check them off after
providing services to patients. A superbill, which may be referred
to as an "encounter form" or "charge ticket," may also include
diagnosis codes, a record of the patient's signature, the patient's
agreement to assign the claim, and the physician's recommendation for subsequent care (for example, "schedule a follow-up visit
in three months"). A copy of this multi-functional document may
also serve as a receipt for the patient.

Understanding the guarantor

Although this chapter refers to "patient" collections, the financial
responsibility is in the hands of a guarantor. A guarantor is a spouse,
family member, or guardian who is the subscriber of the insurance
plan that covers the patient. The patient (and perhaps other family
members) is a beneficiary of the insurance. An example would be a
worker who has family coverage through her employer's health plan.
Her spouse and children would be covered by the health plan as beneficiaries, but she is the guarantor and, thus, the financially responsible party. To keep things simple, we use the term "patient" in this

chapter, but keep in mind that if the patient is not the subscriber, the guarantor is the responsible party.

Time-of-service payments

A time-of-service payment is just that: it's the amount paid when the patient is receiving the service. The amount of time-of-service payment and what services it covers varies, depending on the patient's insurance coverage. Most insurance companies require their beneficiaries to make a nominal payment — known as the copayment, or copay — every time they visit their physician. For physician visits, copayments are usually small amounts (ranging from $10 to $200) and typically don't cover all of the service cost. They are intended to remind patients that there is a cost to seeing a physician, thus discouraging them from seeing the physician for unnecessary visits.

Other payers, such as workers' compensation and most Medicaid plans, do not require any cost-sharing responsibility from their beneficiaries at the time of service. (Notably, some payers require no financial responsibility post-service either.)

Some patients may have copayment responsibilities through their health plan, but time-of-service payment responsibilities are not applied to all services. For example, a patient who had a surgery might not have a required copayment for follow-up visits to check on how they are recovering from the surgery.

For patients who are beneficiaries of a health plan with which your practice participates, your practice has agreed to extend a discount. If your practice participates with a health plan, your charge is discounted to an allowable. The allowable may be 10 percent or more off of your charge, depending on the amount the health plan has agreed to pay its participating providers. For patients who are responsible for a coinsurance, deductible, or non-covered service, you are already extending them a discount in the form of the allowable.

Patients who have no insurance are financially responsible for the entire balance. It's up to your practice to determine whether — and how much — to collect from them at the time of service.

BEST PRACTICES

Let technology help you collect

Technology can assist with collections by means of:

➤ Web-based patient portals and kiosks integrated with payment capability;

➤ Predictive dialers for appointment confirmations and account balances;

➤ Telephonic, automated small balance collections; and

➤ Contract management software that automatically and accurately determines the patient's allowable.

Determining the patient's time-of-service responsibility

Because of the complexity of insurance, the expected amount of the time-of-service payment may be different for every patient. Follow these steps for each patient to ensure that you successfully collect the correct amount:

1. Determine that the patient has insurance. A returning patient has records on file that list his or her insurance information. However, patients change insurance plans — or lose their insurance altogether — because of job changes or unemployment. Ask patients to show their insurance card (or other means of identifying insurance coverage) at each visit.

2. Verify active coverage. Patients may carry cards for health plans that have expired. Insurance cards do not list expiration

dates, so there's no way to tell at a glance whether the card the patient hands you is active. Confirm it by contacting the insurance company, either by telephone or online. This process — confirming active coverage directly with the insurer — is often referred to as "insurance verification."

3. Determine the correct copayment and any other financial responsibility the patient owes. Insurance cards might list the patient's copayment amount for their office visit, but these amounts, too, can change. During the insurance verification process, confirm the patient's financial responsibility directly with the insurance company. Make a note of the copayment, coinsurance, and unmet deductible that the patient owes. If the patient is scheduled to receive a service that may not be covered by his or her health plan, verify eligibility for that benefit. If the health plan does not cover the service, determine the amount that the patient owes for that service, which is the allowable for that CPT code for the patient's insurance company.

4. Query the account balance. Review your practice management system to determine any outstanding balance the patient may owe from previous services. Even if the patient has not yet received a statement for the balance, take the opportunity to inform the patient and attempt to collect.

After you have confirmed the active insurance coverage and accurate financial responsibility, you can ask the patient to make the correct payment.

Take a step back: Pre-visit collections

Unless circumstances dictate otherwise, perform these three steps before the patient presents for the appointment:

1. Determine active insurance, correct plan and service coverage, and copayment, coinsurance, and unmet deductible amounts based on the insurance information the patient provided

FYI

Why business offices make appointment confirmation calls

Given the complexity of insurance billing, some medical practices assign appointment confirmation calls to their business office staff instead of the front office staff. The business office can remind patients of their appointments, as well as monies owed. Plus, they can collect payment over the telephone via a credit card number or they can set up a payment plan. Most importantly, they are in the position to offer a timely, accurate explanation to patients who have questions about their accounts.

during the appointment scheduling process. With the right technology, and the insurance company's cooperation, this process can be performed automatically. If verification is automated, work only those accounts that could not be confirmed.

2. Review each patient's account at least a week before the appointment to determine the account balance that is due.

3. During the appointment confirmation call, explain to the patient what his or her financial responsibility will be. If you cannot confirm that the patient has coverage with a health plan, this pre-visit communication with the patient is a good time to ask if they have alternate coverage. You should explain your practice's payment policies and tell patients who do not have active insurance what they will owe. Alternatively, put the information in writing for the patient, and send the notice about the insurance coverage and amount owed to the patient a week before the appointment.

Pre-visit collections activities support your responsibilities at the front office by ensuring that patients receive timely and accurate communication about their payment responsibility. Setting expectations about payment before the visit means patients are more likely to pay when they arrive.

Patients without insurance

For patients without insurance, often referred to as "self-pay" or "self-insured" patients, it's up to your medical practice to set the collection protocols. These may include one of the following:

➤ Collect 100 percent of the full charge.

➤ Collect a "deposit," which may depend on:

  • Patient's status with your practice (that is, established versus new patient);

  • Service (for example, physical versus problem-focused visit); and

  • Community (for example, if you practice in an impoverished community, charging every uninsured patient $200 for their appointment may not be realistic).

➤ Collect a payment discounted from the physician's full charge if the patient pays that discounted amount at the time of service. Offer a 30 percent discount, for example, to uninsured patients who make payment in full at the time of service.

➤ Offer the patient some financing options. Several financial institutions offer patient financing for medical services; your practice might provide information about one or more of these firms to your patients.

➤ Gather a credit card number. Your practice may contract with a reputable, secure service through its Web-based patient portal, kiosk, or a standalone product so it can automatically debit the patient's credit card when financial responsibility is due.

If the patient is unable to pay, and other options such as credit card deduction, financing and so on, are not available, follow your practice's protocol to establish a payment plan. A payment plan may be as simple as giving the patient an envelope pre-addressed to your business office. Some practices refer patients owing large amounts to a financial counselor or business office team member to discuss the patient's payment options.

Some medical practices apply a "payment in full" protocol at the time of service to patients who carry insurance but who have not been historically responsible for paying their portion of the bills after the service. (Some of the payers with which your practice participates may not allow collecting coinsurance and unmet deductibles at the time of service, so it's important for your practice to put in writing your protocols for negligent patients.)

BEST PRACTICES

Patients who don't pay

Know your practice's policy on dismissing patients who refuse to make a payment or won't establish a payment plan. Many practices dismiss these patients from the practice for non-payment. Some practices continue seeing these patients but require that they pay "cash only" for future care. When those patients are reinstated (after they get their accounts up to date), a practice might charge a small administrative charge as a reinstatement fee. **Caution:** Patients in the middle of a course of treatment by the physicians might have to be handled differently. Dismissal should be handled by a supervisor.

Successfully collecting from patients at the time of service

Most patients are expected to make payment at the time of service, but they don't always want to. So, what should you do when a patient cannot — or will not — make the expected payment? Does your medical practice have signs posted in the reception area saying that say you "expect payment at time of service"? Don't rely on those signs to do the job for you. You must learn how to ask for payments politely but firmly. It is possible to hit the right balance of firmness and courtesy. Learn these techniques to effectively collect from patients at the time of service.

Ask "how" — not "would." Don't unintentionally make it appear that payment at the time of service is optional. Instead of asking, *"Would* you like to pay today?"*, ask, *"How* would you like to pay today?"* Other ways to effectively ask for payment include:

"*Ms. Jones, will it be cash, check, or credit card?*"

"*Ms. Jones, how would you like to take care of your balance?*"

"*Ms. Jones, your insurance company requires us to collect your copayment. How would you like to take care of that today?*"

State the patient's name. Using the patient's name demonstrates that you're focused on the patient. Addressing the person by their salutation (Mr., Mrs., Ms., or Miss) shows you are formal and respectful. All of these impressions help communicate your request for payment.

Look the patient in the eye. Make eye contact when asking for money so patients know you're talking to them and you are serious.

Listen. After you ask for payment, stop talking and start listening. Of course, you want to answer the patient's questions, but, too often, offers of ridiculous payment terms are tendered without allowing patients to explain whether they can pay — or you may talk yourself out of collecting altogether. Let patients tell you how much they can pay. It may be the full amount; it may be less. But don't give the patient a figure your practice would accept for partial payment. After you ask the question, be silent. Allow the patient to respond to your inquiry for payment.

Demonstrate that you expect payment. As you ask the patient for the copayment, deposit, balance due, or other amount, write out the receipt. It shows that you expect to be paid — now.

Reinforce expectations. Your practice has many opportunities to establish expectations for payment at the time of service: in the practice brochure, on the Website, during appointment confirmation calls, and on the registration forms you give to patients to complete. Patients who owe balances and have upcoming appointments may also be called or sent letters that outline their financial responsibility. Those letters and calls also should include a statement that payment is expected at their visit. Don't undo all of those effects when it comes time to collect face-to-face with the patient (see "Scripts for successful collections" later in this chapter). If a patient indicates that he or she isn't aware of your time-of-service payment policy, you can refer to the many places — brochure, Website, appointment confirmation calls, and so forth — your practice states its policy.

Ask for the "due" balance. Don't just focus on collecting past-due accounts, such as an amount that's been owing for 90 days or longer. Be sure to ask for the entire balance, including what's owed for today's visit and any monies that may have come due, whether they are 90 days old or just one.

Have the EOB in hand. When a patient owes a balance based on a deductible that hasn't been met, make sure you have the EOB ready to show. You might politely say,

> *"Ms. Jones, here's the explanation of benefits from the health plan that you chose. You should have received this same explanation in the mail. As you can see, your health plan has transferred the discounted balance to your responsibility. How would you like to take care of it today?"*

If it's too difficult to query and print an EOB from your practice management system for every patient, an alternative is to focus on the balances over an amount set by your practice — perhaps those with more than $500 owing.

Refer to insurance. When patients have questions about the insurer's coverage policies, the amount of the deductible, or any other questions related to their insurance coverage, suggest they call their insurance company. The telephone number for beneficiary inquiries is usually on the insurance card. Provide a telephone for the patient to make the call.

Be ready to help. Be aware of your practice's policies on accepting partial payments or handling patients who cannot or will not pay, but as mentioned before, let the patient make the first offer.

Get an advocate. When patients hesitate to pay, or want to talk about their payment or their financial situation in more depth, steer them to your business office. A face-to-face meeting with a member of your business office staff tells patients they now have a financial advocate. They also get the message that the practice is serious about resolving the outstanding balance. Some practices assign one biller to serve in this role or rotate the responsibility among several billers. Make sure you know to whom you should refer these patients, and how to access that person during office hours. The goal is to arrange for meetings with the business office (or it may be the practice manager) in a private area. Your practice should be able to have these meetings on short notice so there is not a significant delay to the patient's appointment. If possible, identify in advance the patients who may need a meeting with the business office — many practices mark these "problem" accounts in the practice management and scheduling systems. Be sure to communicate payment expectations with those patients over the telephone before the visit, or give these patients "arrival times" that are 15 to 30 minutes before their appointment times so there is time to discuss payment.

Shift blame. There's no nice way to put it — the requirement for a copayment or a deductible is set by the health plan that the patient chose, not your practice. So why stand in the firing line? Be ready to advise patients: "Your insurance company requires us to collect a copayment at the time of service." Or "your health plan applied the balance to your deductible." This tactic gets to the truth of the matter — and it takes you out of the "bad guy" role. It also allows the patient to see that you're only doing what the insurance company requires.

WORDS OF WISDOM

Leveraging the patient's relationship with the payer

Your medical practice signs contracts with many payers, but did you know that patients do too? As part of signing up with a health plan, the patient agrees to certain terms. These include: how much the monthly premium is, what services are covered, and how much the patient is expected pay at each visit. (Often, it is the employer that comes to these terms with the health plan, but the employees who opt for the insurance coverage are then bound to the terms negotiated.) High-performing medical practices know that they can leverage this relationship with patients who forget or refuse to pay their financial obligation. Here are some techniques:

➤ Send a letter to patients who don't pay their copayments. This letter explains that they may be in violation of the contract with their health plan.

➤ Report patients who do not regularly pay copayments or coinsurance to their payers' member services department. Failing to pay copayments likely violates the patient's contract with the health plan.

➤ Emphasize the patient's responsibility. Some medical practices change the signs at the front office from "Payment is Expected at the Time of Service" to "Your Insurance Company Requires Us to Collect a Copayment." The signage emphasizes the reason the patient is required to make the payment.

➤ Institute a financial penalty if the patient fails to make an obligatory payment. The copayment rebilling fee, for example, typically ranges from $10 to $25. If your medical practice intends to implement a penalty for failing to pay at the time of service, patients must be informed of the fee in writing. Most medical practices waive the fee if the patient brings or calls in the payment by the end of the business day. The policy should be made clear during the registration process and via signs around the reception area. For example, the practice could post a sign that states: "Your insurance company requires us to collect a copayment. If you are unable to pay your copayment at the time of service, there will be an additional $20 fee."

Discuss all forms of payment. Don't forget to mention all forms of payment your practice accepts in addition to cash. These may include credit cards, debit cards, and personal checks. Credit card companies take a small fee from each payment that a merchant (including a physician) accepts via credit card. Even though your physician is sacrificing that percentage of each credit card charge, it's far less money than it would cost for staff to send a series of billing statements and write off the bad debt from patients who won't pay after they've left your practice. For personal checks, your practice may have a protocol to follow for patients who have previously written checks with insufficient funds. A reliable way to ensure there are no bounced checks is to use an automated check verification service.

Thank the patient. Show your appreciation for patients who pay by thanking them: "Ms. Jones, thank you for making your payment today."

Provide a receipt. Print or write out a receipt for all monies accepted at the time of service, and give it to the patient.

Maintain the record of payments. Your practice keeps a detailed record (see Exhibit 6.1, Time-of-Service Payment Log) of all payments, separated by cash, check, and credit card. Before the end of the day (or the shift, in the event of staffing changes), it is necessary to compare the payments received to the log of payments and the monies that are recorded on the superbills or posted to the practice management system. If cash was provided at the beginning of the day to make change, ensure that this money is accounted for. This procedure, often referred to as "balancing," should be detailed in writing by the practice for all staff to follow consistently (see Exhibit 6.2, Deposit Log). Ideally, this task should be performed by or under the close direction of a supervisor. This procedure is an important part of the practice's internal controls to prevent loss of money. Big problems occur when front office team members are sloppy or get in a rush and fail to accurately record collected amounts.

Use collection monitoring to improve. Your supervisor or the business office likely keeps track of the amount of money collected at the front office by each team member. Reports on these collections are made weekly or monthly. The reports also compare the amount actually collected with what was expected to be collected. You can learn the results of your efforts and work to improve over time.

Use rescheduling protocols. Sometimes when patients owe money or cannot make their copayment, your practice may want you to ask them to reschedule their appointment instead of being seen that day. Be sure you know the protocols used to determine which, if any, patients should be rescheduled in the following cases.

> ➤ *Ill patient:* Some patients might be sick and should not wait to be seen. Some medical practices involve clinical staff in making these types of decisions.

> ➤ *Type of visit scheduled:* The type of visit may help to decide whether to reschedule the non-paying patient. For example, someone coming in for a preventive visit, like a physical, isn't in urgent need of care. Based on the type of visit (preventive),

| [EXHIBIT 6.1] | Time-of-service payment log |

Your Name:

Date:

Patient Name	Account Number	Amount Due	Form of Payment (CC, Cash, Check)	Amount Paid

Total Cash	$
Total Credit card	$
Total Check	$
TOTAL Paid	$

Use these totals to help you prepare the "deposit log"

Instructions: Please record every payment you receive on this log. Please also mark the "amount paid" and the form of payment on the charge ticket. You must provide a written receipt to all patients. Please note that you must complete this "time-of-service payment log" and balance it at the end of every clinic — before you leave for lunch and before you leave for the evening.

[EXHIBIT 6.2]	Deposit log

Your Name:

Date:

Total charges: $ _____

Total cash: $ _____

Total credit cards: $ _____

Total checks: $ _____

Total payments: $ _____

Instructions: Sum and record the charges from all charge tickets. Sum and record the cash, credit cards, and checks. "Total payments" must equal the sum of "total cash," "total credit cards," and "total checks." Attach charge tickets, payment (divided by form of payment), and your tapes to this form. Return the form and attachments to your supervisor. Please note that you must complete this "deposit log" at the end of every clinic — before you leave for lunch and before you leave for the evening.

---

they could be safely rescheduled. On the other hand, someone scheduled for an acute complaint may have a serious problem; they should not be automatically rescheduled just because they are behind on their payment or don't have their bank card with them.

Your medical practice should have a protocol to guide you in handling patients who owe money but present without funds. Ideally, this policy should be in writing and distributed to patients, such as in the new patient registration packets. Most importantly, this policy should be both clinically appropriate and consistent with your malpractice carrier's requirements. For these reasons, it is important that

BEST PRACTICES

What to do when you cannot collect

Develop an "If Not, Why Not" report. When you can't collect a payment, document why you weren't successful. Turn in the report every day, and review it with your coworkers and a supervisor. Discuss ways that you can improve your time-of-service collection efforts.

BEST PRACTICES

When a divorced parent says the other parent will pay

For children of divorced parents, collection can be difficult. Often, the parent who accompanies the child reports that the payment is the responsibility of the other parent. Many parents even refer to their divorce decree and/or their attorney to justify not paying. What should you do? Tell them that it is the policy of your practice that the parent who accompanies the child is responsible for payment. The terms of a divorce are a private matter between the child's parents or guardians — your practice is not a party to that private agreement. Because this situation happens often, your practice should have this policy in writing to set expectations for the parents and guardians of all patients.

The policy might read:

> The parent who consents to the treatment of a minor child is responsible for payment of the services rendered. Medical Practice Associates will not be involved in custody, separation, or divorce disputes.

Please note that you need to confer with an attorney regarding any state regulations that may dictate your policy.

you understand this policy, follow it, and ask a supervisor for clarification whenever you are unsure.

In addition to patient rescheduling, determine what your medical practice's policy is regarding scheduling patients who are in bad-debt status or who have been sent to the collection agency. If these patients are to continue to be seen, determine whether the business office staff is expected to attempt collection of the new charges. For many practices, the patient's new charge must be paid in full before being seen.

The check-out desk

The staff member who is assisting a patient checking out of the practice offers another resource in collecting from the patient. Chapter 8, Check-out, discusses this and other check-out tasks in more detail. Here are the check-out functions that directly relate to time-of-service payments, which you may be assigned to handle.

Asking for money at check-out is especially handy in the following circumstances:

- ➤ For patients who receive services that are not covered by their health plan, often referred to as "non-covered services," and were not anticipated when the appointment was scheduled;

- ➤ For patients who owe a coinsurance that must be calculated based on a percentage of the allowables associated with the services rendered by the practice; and

- ➤ For patients for whom the amount owed is tied to the service that they are rendered — for example, extra labs for a self-pay patient who already paid for his or her physical.

There may be other circumstances where you cannot determine the amount the patient owes before he or she is seen. For practices that have many patients who fall in one of these categories, collecting all monies at the check-out desk (versus incorporating it as the patient checks in) works more effectively.

The check-out desk does give you a final opportunity to collect from patients before they walk out the door. It is important to request and collect these payments — or at least initiate payment plans for patients who owe large amounts but do not have the funds — because billing for them later is an expense to your practice.

Remember, monies collected at the time of service reduce your practice's billing costs, as well as the days in accounts receivable. The more dollars you collect at the front office, the better your practice's overall revenue performance.

 BEST PRACTICES

Help calculating allowables

For most insured patients, your practice's services are rendered at a discounted rate — the allowable. Unfortunately, there is no standard allowable — the rates differ by procedure code and often by place of service. They also can differ by insurance company, and even within an insurance company, as dictated by the health plans each insurance company may offer in the local market. To help staff calculate the allowable, many practices provide a spreadsheet of the allowables by major health plan for commonly billed procedure codes. Another method is to contract with a vendor for software that calculates and displays these rates automatically. You should familiarize yourself with the tools that your practice offers to determine the patient's financial responsibility.

Scripts for successful collections

Collecting cash from patients doesn't just happen. You have to ask. The key is to balance courtesy with firmness. To help you, scripts for the several different collections scenarios that often arise are provided in Appendix 6A.

Use these scripts as models for rehearsing what to say to patients in the common situations that always seem come up when collecting copayments, deductibles, or other payments due at the time of service. Look to your practice's own protocols to determine which scripts to use and how to modify the message to be successful at collecting time-of-service payments.

Conclusion

Collecting payments from patients while they are still in the office helps your practice avoid expenses and delays in getting paid. Motivated front office staff members are the key ingredients in making these in-office collection efforts succeed. By understanding your responsibilities and mastering the techniques of time-of-service collections, you can make a measurable contribution to your practice's financial success.

Appendix 6A: Scripts for Success — Collections

The following scripts are provided as samples only. Discuss your practice's protocols for these situations with your supervisor.

Collection at time of service: Insured patient (optional with deductible owing). You say:

"Mr./Ms. [patient/responsible party's name], our practice's policy is to request payment at the time of service. Your insurance plan requires a copayment of $_____ and you have a deductible of $_____. Your total today is $_____. Will you be paying with cash, check, or credit card?"

After receiving payment, respond with:

"Thank you, Mr./Ms. _____, for your payment. If there is a balance still remaining after your insurance company pays its portion of your charges today, we will send a statement for the balance. Our policy is for any billed payments to be made within 10 days of receiving the bill. We appreciate your cooperation."

Collection at time of service: Full-paying patient (self-paying — not insured). You say:

"Mr./Ms. _____, our practice's policy is to request payment at the time of service. Your estimated amount for today's service is $_____. Will you be paying with cash, check, or credit card today?"

Responses to common objections made by patients

If the patient says:

"I never had to pay at one my visits here before."

Respond with:

"Mr./Ms. [patient/responsible party's name], I understand your concern, but our office procedure has changed because of rising costs. Paying at the time of service keeps our administrative costs from going higher so we don't have to charge more for our services. Plus, it lets you take care

of your payment now rather than waiting for a bill. Would you like to pay by cash, check, or credit card?"

If the patient says:

"My insurance will pay."

If... the patient is from a contracted health plan with a copayment required, respond with:

"Mr./Ms. _____, based on the contract we have with your insurance company, you have a copayment amount that is your responsibility. Would you like to pay that by cash, check, or credit card?"

If... after verifying the patient's coverage with the insurance company, a copayment, coinsurance, and/or deductible are owing, respond with:

"Mr./Ms. _____, when we verified your insurance coverage, the company representative said there is deductible/coinsurance/copayment that is your responsibility at the time of service. Would you like to pay that by cash, check, or credit card?"

If... coverage is NOT verified but the insurance card indicates a copayment amount, respond with:

"Mr./Ms. _____, your insurance card indicates a copayment amount that is your responsibility. Would you like to pay that by cash, check, or credit card?"

If the patient says:

"I didn't bring my purse/wallet/checkbook/credit card, etc."

Respond with:

"That's okay, Mr./Ms. _____. We accept checks, cash, or credit cards. Do you have one of those with you today?"

If... the patient says "no," respond with:

"How were you planning to pay today?"

If... the patient says "by credit card, but I don't have it with me today," respond with:

"That's okay, Mr./Ms. _____. Would you like to call home [or your spouse, parent] for your credit card number?"

If... the patient says "by check, but I don't have my checkbook today," respond with:

"Here is our practice's self-addressed stamped envelope for your convenience. Could you please write the check to [name of physician/ practice] when you get home and mail it today in this envelope?"

If the patient says:

"My ex-spouse is responsible for my/our child's medical bills."

Respond with:

"I understand, Mr./Ms. _____, that your former husband/wife may have agreed to pay these expenses, but that is an agreement between you and him/her. I can give you a duplicate receipt for your payment today so you can get reimbursed. How would you like to pay today: cash, check, or credit card?"

If the patient says:

"I am not able to pay the full amount now; can I pay over time?"

Your response (depending on your practice's financial policy) may be:

"Mr./Ms. _____, how much time do you need?"

If... your practice requires a 50 percent payment and the remainder in 30 days, respond with:

"Mr./Ms. _____, we will accept half the amount of your charge today and we will bill you for the balance in 30 days. Are you going to use cash, check, or credit card for today's payment?"

If... the patient is full-pay (self-pay), respond with:

"Mr./Ms. _____, if you pay the charge owing in full today, our policy is to give a discount of [discount percent]."

If the patient says:

"This practice seems more concerned about getting payment than about my care."

Respond with:

"Mr./Ms. _____, our first concern is your care. Getting payment for that care ensures that we can continue providing quality treatment that you and our other patients expect. Would you like to pay by cash, check, or credit card?"

If the patient says:

"Just send me a bill."

Respond with:

"Mr./Ms. _____, our practice's policy is to collect payment at the time of service. How would you like to pay: cash, check, or credit card?"

CHAPTER 6 QUIZ

Multiple Choice

Choose the one correct answer to each question.

1. Pre-visit collections efforts may include:
   a. A reminder about expected payment during the appointment confirmation call
   b. A letter describing the patient's financial responsibility for services to be rendered at the patient's next appointment
   c. Insurance verification
   d. All of the above

2. An EOB is an:
   a. Explanation of benefits
   b. Explanation of beneficiary
   c. Entire outstanding balance
   d. Electronic online billing

3. Dealing with patients who owe funds but cannot pay should be:
   a. Put in writing as a practice protocol
   b. Very flexible
   c. Handled by the county health department
   d. None of the above

4. The procedure called "balancing" should:
   a. Be done at the end of every day (or shift)
   b. Follow a written procedure
   c. Ideally, be done by or under the close direction of a supervisor
   d. All of the above

5. When a medical practice requires patients who owe money to reschedule their appointments, a common protocol is to:
   a. Put their names on the Website
   b. See them anyway if they are ill
   c. Call the police
   d. All of the above

Matching

Enter the letter of the correct definition from the right column next to the term in the left column that is the best match.

1. __ Allowable

2. __ CPT

3. __ Deductible

4. __ Non-covered service

5. __ Superbill

a. An amount that must be paid on an annual basis before the patient's insurance company commences payment.

b. A service for which the insurance company will not pay, and for which the patient is responsible to pay.

c. An electronic or paper ticket that lists the codes that a physician commonly uses.

d. The reimbursement level that is contractually agreed to by the practice and the insurance company.

e. The acronym for Current Procedural Terminology; each service provided by a physician is given a "code."

Math Problems

1. Mr. Walker owes $83.25. His health plan requires a 20 percent coinsurance. How much does he owe? Answer: _____

2. Mrs. Smith owes $345.81. Her health plan requires a 15 percent coinsurance. How much does she owe?
   Answer: _____

3. The mother of Jill Brown is the guarantor for her daughter's account. The services that Jill received equal $1,765.03. Her mother's health plan requires a 33 percent coinsurance. How much does Jill's mother owe? Answer: _____

4. Mr. Wood does not have insurance, but he would like to take advantage of your discount for uninsured patients who pay in full at the time of service. His bill is $213.00, and your practice offers a 30 percent discount for payment in full. How much does he owe? Answer: _____

Answers to this quiz are in Appendix B.

CHAPTER 7

Waiting:
Managing the Patient's Wait

Have you ever had to wait a long time for a physician? Or maybe you stood in line at the Department of Motor Vehicles, or got stuck on an airplane that sat on the runway for a few hours? What aggravated you the most? Oftentimes, it is the uncertainty and powerlessness you feel in these situations that makes them seem much worse. When patients have to wait, good communications — honest and open — by staff can help smooth some of the hard feelings.

In Chapter 3, Registration, we talk about ways to make the registration and check-in processes run smoothly so there are not delays for patients trying to check in. In this chapter, we look at ways you can help make it easier for patients when they have to wait to see the physician.

Even when the office runs on time, there is always some waiting at a medical practice. Occasionally, there are delays you cannot control, such as patient emergencies that cause physicians and other medical providers to fall behind schedule. In this chapter, we look at how to manage both situations: normal waits and unpredictable delays. It is your responsibility to help manage those waits.

BEST PRACTICES

Know your reception services factors

There are many things that can delay patients that may not be under your control. All the same, it's wise to know about them in advance. To help assess the waiting factors of your practice, take a look at this checklist that management consultants use when assessing a medical practice's customer service.

❑ Is parking adequate?

❑ Are the grounds maintained and kept free of debris?

❑ Is the entrance accessible?

❑ Is the reception area clean, neat, and quiet?

❑ Is the receptionist welcoming? Does he or she make eye contact?

❑ Are patients greeted with enthusiasm, respect, and concern?

❑ Is there adequate space to wait?

Wait management

A medical practice provides a service to customers. The certainty of an automobile assembly line — one part every 6.3 minutes, for example — simply doesn't exist. Although a medical practice establishes a schedule, patients' arrival times rarely match up exactly. Some patients arrive early; others are late. Plus, the nature of taking care of patients — versus placing the same screw on the same car part — means that service times vary. Consequently, so does the wait.

Because waiting is, in essence, a given for your patients, it's your goal to make it manageable for them. "Managing" the wait means that you'll minimize it — and you'll make sure that the patient is comfortable and informed while waiting.

Let's start off with managing the quality of the patient's wait.

BEST PRACTICES

Understand wait time

"Wait time" is a measure of the time from the patient's arrival to the practice until the patient is escorted to the exam room. Although some practices vary in the measurement (for example, waiting until the registration process is completed by the patient), the waiting time is — and should be — a reflection of the patient's wait. Measure your patients' wait time, and compare it to industry benchmarks, such as those published by Press Ganey Associates (see Exhibit 7.1).

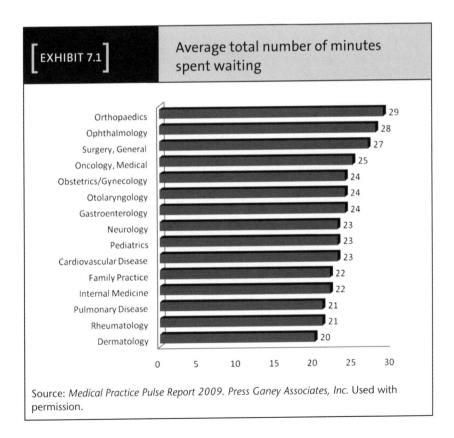

[EXHIBIT 7.1] Average total number of minutes spent waiting

Specialty	Minutes
Orthopaedics	29
Ophthalmology	28
Surgery, General	27
Oncology, Medical	25
Obstetrics/Gynecology	24
Otolaryngology	24
Gastroenterology	24
Neurology	23
Pediatrics	23
Cardiovascular Disease	23
Family Practice	22
Internal Medicine	22
Pulmonary Disease	21
Rheumatology	21
Dermatology	20

Source: *Medical Practice Pulse Report 2009. Press Ganey Associates, Inc.* Used with permission.

FYI

Estimating time

If the wait time is 30 minutes, should you say:

A. "The doctor will be right with you;"

B. "Your wait will be 15 minutes," or

C. "Your wait time will be 35 minutes"?

The answer is C. Never, ever, underestimate time; if you have to give a time, overestimate a little. Avoid the phrase: "The doctor will be right with you" — unless it's actually true!

Change your "waiting room" to a "reception area." Changing what you call the area where patients wait before their appointment helps to create a new attitude for everyone — you and your patients. Support this by changing signage, as well as how you refer to the area. Instead of giving patients the perception that you expect them to wait; you communicate: "we're ready to receive you."

Greet patients warmly. The root word of "receptionist" is *to receive,* so do it. Don't "arrive" your patients; receive them. Use the patient's name at every opportunity. Welcome patients with a smile, a short greeting, and eye contact. This "moment of truth" defines the patients' perception of your practice. If your interaction is a pleasant one, they are more likely to accept a reasonable wait for services.

Keep patients informed. Keep patients informed about their wait. Even if long waits are inevitable in your practice, most of the customer service challenges can be reduced by being proactive and open about delays. Patients might tolerate longer waits to see a physician than for other types of services, but that doesn't mean they are happy about waiting. Even though waits of 20 minutes or more have become the average in many practices, that's no reason to take the patient's time for granted. When delays occur, please don't resort to the commonly used statement, "the doctor will be right with you." For patients who have been waiting more than 15 minutes, do the following:

1. Notify them of the delay by either approaching them in the reception area or, if you cannot leave your workstation, pleasantly call them up to the front window to explain.

2. Apologize for the delay.

3. Estimate the additional wait time. Always overestimate the wait time by a few minutes; your patients will be delighted that the wait was shorter than you had anticipated. Repeat this communication every 15 minutes, and patients will handle the wait much better because they know you respect their time.

 WORDS OF WISDOM

A great idea! Tracking wait times

With so many patients checking in, it may seem impossible to track the time that every patient has been waiting in order to keep them informed. A solution to this dilemma exists in the form of inexpensive digital timers with magnetic clips. Start the timer as soon as the patient arrives; if you can't, make sure you recognize that patients have already been waiting a few minutes, so you should adjust your communications with them accordingly. Place the timer on a clipboard with the patient's name and keep them on the chart rack. Alternately, jot down the patient's name on a magnetic white board and place the timer on top. You'll see at a glance who has been waiting the longest. In essence, find a way to designate a timer for each patient. As patients are brought to the back, stop the timer, erase the name, and continue the rotation.

Open the window. It shouldn't be any surprise that patients become lost or forgotten when you place a physical barrier between you and them. A barrier, even a window, makes it harder for you to visually survey the reception area to notice the patient who has been waiting too long, much less gauge the mood of the room.

Maintain the area. Attend to the neat placement of current magazines around the reception area. Ideally, your practice should stock the reception area with magazines that are relevant to your patients and the persons accompanying them by economic status, age, educational background, and native languages. Additional maintenance steps in caring for the area are to keep plants healthy, pick up litter, and clean walls and furniture as needed. Pay special attention to cleanliness in the children's area if your practice offers one. Pick up trash at lunch and after office hours. Someone should be responsible for walking through the reception area before the doors open for patients, and then frequently throughout the day to tidy up.

By managing the quality of the patient's wait, you can cut down on the frustration that the patient may be feeling while waiting — and perhaps even turn it into a positive impression.

More ways to manage the wait

There are many other ways that you can try to make waiting less bothersome for patients. Several of these additional tactics may require a decision by management to implement, but, if so, you are likely to be the person who makes the idea work. Let's take a look at these methods — some new, some old — and what to look for when using them to manage the wait.

Create a pleasant atmosphere. Natural lighting; soft, soothing music; comfortable furniture; an agreeable temperature; clean, accessible restrooms; and a calming color palette for walls, carpet, furniture, and interior decorations are all welcomed by patients who have to wait. If your practice serves children, define a separate area for sick children.

Add amenities. Your reception area should provide entertainment or at least enough diversions to occupy your patients as they wait. Other ways to make the wait go faster for patients include adding:

➤ A wireless network for patients to use their own laptops;

➤ Robes and slippers (useful for replacing paper gowns, particularly those given to patients for a sub-waiting area);

➤ Patient education materials;

➤ Computers loaded with materials relevant to the practice;

➤ Simple games on paper, such as Sudoku, crossword puzzles, and word search puzzles that help pass the time (create your own puzzles using Websites for educators);

➤ Notepads for adults with your logo and coloring books for children;

➤ Jigsaw puzzles (but not if your practice serves children who could choke on small pieces);

➤ Carnival mirrors, books, and a toy bin for children (but make sure toys are safe for all ages and are not left where other patients could stumble on them). Be sure to clean toys routinely to prevent spreading germs;

➤ Water or a coffee bar, with a machine that offers self-serve specialty coffee drinks (but not if your practice serves small children);

➤ An aquarium with colorful fish, turtles, or other aquatic animals;

➤ A working train on tracks suspended from the ceiling (for added affect, provide a "start" button on the wall for patients to push and decorate the train based on the seasons);

➤ Stationery to write a note to a friend or relative (offer to stamp and mail it if the patient has addressed it); and

➤ Recipe and coupon exchange boxes.

Hand out pagers. Allow patients to get up and walk around if there is an outdoor walking area adjacent to the practice. Pagers that combine simple video games are appreciated (as long as the sound can be muted). Embed your pagers in a large (10-inch diameter) holding device, such as a piece of wood, if theft is a possibility. For practices that serve children, cut the wood into a shape to fit a theme, such as a boat or fish.

Host an "art gallery." Ask local artists to display their work — or perhaps some of your staff or patients who are painters, photographers, quilters, and so forth. Frame school projects of staff's and physicians' children to hang on the walls. Hold a photography contest for staff (or even patients) to enter. Recruit art students from a local college to paint a mural in a hallway. In addition to showcasing local talent, your reception area gets decorated for free.

Post pictures. Photographs of you, the physicians, and other members of your practice's team with some professional and personal information can help establish a "personal" relationship between patients and your practice. Try posting your baby pictures; patients will be delighted.

Entertain. Television can entertain, but some thought should be put into what channels to show and at what volume. If you have room, build a small movie "theater" into your reception area to play movies that you have screened for content and age level.

"Hire" a volunteer. A local retirement center may know someone who wants to volunteer as a greeter in your reception area — something hospitals have done successfully for years. Your volunteer could serve coffee, read to children, hold the door for the mother shepherding small children, or fetch a pen for someone filling out a form. Alternatively, ask a former patient to volunteer to perform the same duties.

Infuse pleasant smells. Use an air purifier to remove the "clinical" smell that pervades most practices. If you have the resources, bake muffins or bread in your reception area. Offer the baked goods to patients. Not only are patients delighted with the treat, the smell provides a wonderful aroma.

Improving the quality of the wait adds value for the patient. Be creative in suggestions to your supervisor. Consider the population of patients you serve — and those new patients your physicians hope to attract. Come up with ideas that can improve the patient's wait. Improvements don't have to bust the budget because, often, just a few minor touches can improve the atmosphere of the reception area.

 WORDS OF WISDOM

Other ways for medical practices to add value to the "wait"

Some activities for patients while they wait can add value to their medical care. Many medical practices offer waiting patients these items:

➤ Blank forms with the heading:

- "Issues I wish to discuss with my doctor today" — helps patients focus on what they will say to the physician; and/or
- "Medications I would like to renew" — so patients won't forget to mention them when they see their physician.

➤ Patient education materials — helps patients learn a little more about their medical issues.

➤ A medical history form to complete — saves time and improves information flow during the pre-exam preparation by the medical assistant or nurse.

Managing unpredictable delays

Sometimes, small, expected waits become long ones because of an emergency or unexpected event. Here are the steps to manage unpredictable delays:

1. Get information about physician delays as quickly as possible. Too often, the clinical support staff hears about a physician's delay but forgets — or doesn't think — to let you or another team member at the front office know. Your practice benefits by having a protocol to make sure that *everyone* knows what's happening with the physicians' schedules. A "group" e-mail address such as alert-delay@yourpracticename.com can be established for this use.

2. Encourage a member of the clinical support team, such as a nurse or medical assistant, to deliver the news of a delay to waiting patients. In some practices, the delayed physician delivers the news too. Many management experts recommend this. It only takes a few seconds for the late-arriving physician to step into the reception area to apologize for the delay, thank the patients for waiting, and promise to be with them as soon as possible.

3. Immediately give significantly delayed patients the choice of rescheduling or waiting. People tend to feel less put-upon when they have a choice. Talk to your supervisor about defining "significant" — 30 minutes? 60 minutes? — for your practice. If necessary, ask if other staff can help temporarily in the front office with rescheduling.

4. Plan to telephone any scheduled patients who may be affected by the delay. (Be sure your practice is capturing cellular phone numbers for all patients; this makes your job in reaching the patient much easier!) Give patients who have not yet arrived the opportunity to reschedule if it appears the delay may be lengthy.

Good management of the waiting process will never make people enjoy delays, but it can keep them from getting aggravated about the situation.

BEST PRACTICES

Learn to apologize

What's the most effective way to calm down a patient who is complaining? It is to simply say you are sorry. Unfortunately, it's often difficult for many employees to apologize when the problem is not their fault. This emotion is completely understandable. You don't have to embrace the blame; instead say, "Thank you for bringing that to our attention. I'm sorry that we didn't meet your expectations." It's an apology that doesn't identify blame.

Reducing wait times

In addition to improving the quality of the wait, it's also important to minimize the amount of the patient's wait. A portion of the patient's wait is based on the processing time in the front office. Patients must wait while you pull up their account, scan applicable cards and documents, and hand over registration and medical history paperwork. Although these are important tasks, patients appreciate it if these tasks can be performed more efficiently. With some process changes, you may be able to accomplish these tasks more quickly — and thus, decrease the patient's waiting time too.

Here are some process changes to think about (your practice may already have the technology to make many of these suggestions happen):

➤ Automate the sign-in and arrival processes.

➤ Reduce the amount of or combine the paperwork that patients must complete.

➤ Capture the patients' signature electronically — only once.

➤ Pre-register patients by telephone, kiosk, or Web-based patient portal.

➤ Use resources, such as a high-speed scanner and dual computer monitor screens for staff, so you can reduce the time it takes to register a patient.

It's good business practice to figure out if the changes made were worth doing. Reevaluate the process time after making any changes. Be sure to check that the portions of the process you changed are running smoothly before you do an evaluation. It's important to recognize that work flow won't be perfected with a sweep of a wand or a couple of changes to a process. Improving efficiency — and reducing the patient's wait time — is a series of many small changes that combine to make improvements. As they add up, these changes optimize your patients' perceptions of value. In other words, patients will be glad they came and will recommend your practice to their family and friends.

Late arrivals

Your practice is a service business — not an automobile factory — so you should expect that some patients will show up late for appointments. Instead of tolerating late patients, many medical practices address this problem directly.

Create a window. Most practices consider the patient late when 15 minutes has passed. You need to discuss this time frame with your supervisor. Once your practice chooses a time, stick to it unless there are extenuating circumstances. If parking is scarce because of an event in your building, the elevator is out of order, or traffic is particularly heavy around your practice, patients should be given some grace time. To prevent these problems from disrupting the schedule, be sure to tell patients to allow for extra time when you're on the telephone with them at the time they schedule their appointment.

Offer options. Instead of automatically turning late arrivers away, consider offering patients who show up more than 15 minutes after their appointment time the opportunity to reschedule or wait to be seen. Set appropriate expectations that the appointment will be when the physician finds time, which could be an hour or two. Some may reschedule; others might want to wait to be worked in. Either way, they will feel like you accommodated them and provided good service. Best of all, you prevent the late-arriving patient from inconveniencing other patients.

Prevent late arrivals. Set expectations about promptness when patients make appointments and when appointment confirmation calls are made. Suggested messages could be: "Your appointment is at 8:30 Thursday morning; please allow time for parking and traffic." Better yet, say, "The arrival time for your appointment with Dr. Jones is 8:15." Stating the time when you want the patient there — 8:15 — is much better than giving them another time (8:30) and telling them to come early.

This also is a good time to warn patients of any road construction near your practice that may cause delays. Also advise them regarding:

➤ Whether parking is a problem at certain times of the day;

➤ The best places to look for parking; and

➤ Any other transportation issues (public or private) about which other patients have been complaining recently.

Fix internal problems. Practices that want to convince patients to always show up on time should make sure their own house is in order. You won't convince patients that promptness matters if *you* routinely run late. When physicians consistently run late, the percentage of late-arriving patients accelerates. Besides, if you always run 30 minutes behind, it's difficult to justify turning away someone who is just 15 minutes late. Physicians who are meticulously on time never complain about patients who are late because they rarely, if ever, have such patients.

Target the worst offenders. Some patients *always* show up late. Your supervisor may ask you to help identify these patients by making a note in the practice management system in the records of patients who show up late. Practice management systems usually have a field for special notes, sometimes called "account alert notes" or something similar. Set up the code "CLA" for "chronic late arriver." When those habitually late patients call to schedule other appointments later on, you'll know who they are. Avoid scheduling these patients for late in the afternoon or the first appointment of the day. This helps keep that habitual late arriver from forcing everyone to stay late or getting behind schedule at the start of the day.

Conclusion

You can't turn your practice into an automobile factory with predictable arrival times for the parts, but you can help manage the patient's wait time by reducing the patient's wait — and improving the quality of it.

CHAPTER 7 QUIZ

True or False

Circle the correct answer.

1. It is not the receptionist's responsibility to help improve the quality of the wait for patients. T **F**

2. A receptionist who makes eye contact when greeting patients is a factor in how patients judge the quality of service a medical practice provides. T **F**

3. Even though patients are given appointment times, some arrive late and some arrive early. T **F**

4. It's best to not tell patients there is a delay because doing so makes them more upset. **T** F

5. A barrier between the receptionist and the waiting room — even clear glass — makes it harder to keep tabs on the "mood" of the waiting room and who's been waiting too long. T   **F**

6. When a physician is late, the best statement you can make to a patient is: "the doctor will be right with you." **T** F

Multiple Choice

Choose the one correct answer to each question.

1. Factors that influence patients' opinions about the service they are getting include:
   a. Clean, neat, and quiet reception area
   b. Receptionist who welcomes patients to the practice
   c. Adequate space to wait
   d. All of the above

2. Suggested ways to entertain patients while they wait to see their physician can include:
   a. Computers loaded with educational materials relevant to the practice
   b. Coloring books for children
   c. An aquarium with colorful fish, turtles, or other aquatic animals
   d. All of the above

3. A recommended technique to prevent late-arriving patients from disrupting the physician's schedule is to:
   a. Refuse to see patients who arrive more than five minutes after their appointment time
   b. Set expectations by requesting on-time arrival when scheduling appointments and making reminder calls
   c. Offer gifts and discounts for prompt arrivals
   d. All of the above

4. Which of the following actions is NOT recommended when a delay causes patients to wait longer?
   a. Notify them of the delay
   b. Apologize for the delay
   c. Estimate the additional wait time (slightly overestimating the time)
   d. Never explain the reason for delay

5. When there is a long and unexpected delay for patients, this chapter recommends:
   a. Giving patients information as quickly as possible
   b. Encouraging a nurse or medical assistant to deliver news of the delay
   c. Offering to reschedule appointments
   d. All of the above

Matching

Enter the letter of the correct definition from the right column next to the term in the left column that is the best match.

1. __ Amenities
2. __ Atmosphere
3. __ Reception area
4. __ Maintenance
5. __ Pre-register
6. __ Kiosk

a. A different name for the "waiting room," intended to make a positive service impression.

b. Asking patients to complete forms (online or on paper) before they come to their appointments.

c. Actions (such as cleaning and tidying up) by staff to keep a reception area pleasant.

d. Activities, distractions, and services that are pleasing (puzzles, wireless Internet, coffee bar, etc.) and help make the wait go faster for patients.

e. A free-standing computer-equipped station in the reception area where patients can do most of the check-in process themselves.

f. Lighting, paint color, and decorations that make the reception area more soothing and pleasant to wait in.

Answers to this quiz are in Appendix B.

CHAPTER 8

Check-out:
Handling the Patient's Exit

Check-out is the patient's last stop in the medical visit, but it is certainly an important one. Staff members at the check-out desk — which can be physically located at or around the corner from the practice's front desk — provide administrative support to the clinical team by finalizing the specifics of the physician's recommended treatment plan. Depending on how your practice has organized its various functions, you may be responsible for the following functions at check-out:

➤ Ensuring the completion of charge-entry tasks for services the patient has just received;

➤ Scheduling a subsequent visit for the patient with his or her physician;

➤ Completing paperwork and possibly scheduling for a patient referred to other physicians, testing, ancillary providers, or for other services such as surgery;

➤ Performing the steps to gain insurance approval of any procedures or diagnostics (such as ultrasound, MRIs, etc.) that the physician has requested for the patient;

➤ Confirming that the patient has received information he or she needs, such as patient education brochures, handouts or other materials;

➤ Calculating and collecting payments that are the patient's financial responsibility, including outstanding balances, coinsurance, etc.;

STEPS TO GET THERE

Check-out checklist

The check-out function plays a critical role in ensuring that patients get necessary information, physician orders are implemented, and important functions, including appointment scheduling and collections, are completed. Look through this checklist to see if you and your practice's check-out team have the tools, training, and information needed.

❑ Is the patient handled in a timely and courteous manner?

❑ Are patient lines kept to a minimum?

❑ Does the patient have to be asked about post-encounter instructions, or is such provided in a legible format by the provider?

❑ Does the patient understand all instructions about the next steps in their plan of care, to include additional appointments and ancillaries?

❑ Is the patient asked to schedule a follow-up appointment?

❑ Is the patient asked if he or she needs letters, work or school excuses, prescription renewals, referrals, or testing before the patient exits?

❑ Is there a customer service question asked at the end of check-out (for example, "Is there anything else I can help you with today?")?

❑ Is a receipt provided for any time-of-service payment requested?

❑ Does the patient know what to expect regarding the results of ancillary tests, to include when, how, and from whom the results will be delivered?

❑ How, when, and by whom are charges keyed into the practice management system?

❑ Is there a process to ensure that all services rendered by providers are captured, coded, and billed, to include outstanding balances for the day's visit and previous visits?

➤ Serving as the primary responder to telephone calls — or backing up the operator; and

➤ Responding to patient requests for more information about payment, appointment scheduling, and so on.

Regardless of what functions your practice incorporates into your check-out station, this position is important for your practice — and its patients.

Information

The information you help give the patient at the check-out desk can save time and money for the practice. Why? You and your coworkers spend a large part of each day answering telephone calls. As Chapter 4, Telephones, explains, a good number of these calls could be prevented by anticipating patients' questions — and proactively providing the information so they don't even have to call and ask. The best place to do this is when the patient is still at your practice. Because the check-out desk is the last stop in the patient's visit to the practice, it is an ideal opportunity to make sure questions have been answered, forms have been provided, and so on.

Make sure patients receive every piece of information they may need before they leave the practice site after their visit is over. When a patient has to call back for more information after the visit, you and the clinical staff, including nurses, spend more time:

➤ Locating the information the patient wants to know about, which could involve billing, scheduling, or clinical staff;

➤ Referring medical questions to the clinical staff and, if necessary, finding the patient's medical record so it can be checked before giving the answer;

➤ Calling back the patient with the proper answer; and

➤ Making sure that if any new medical information was given
to the patient over the telephone, a new note is added to the
medical record about it.

Staff working at the check-out desk can play a critical role in reducing the volume of what are many times unnecessary callbacks. You
can help by completing the scheduling of appointments, tests, and
referrals; confirming and collecting payments; and processing applicable insurance requirements. Most importantly, you perform the
responsibilities to which you are assigned accurately and completely.
If you fail to do so, patients will be frustrated — and you and your
colleagues will end up with more work!

 STEPS TO GET THERE

Information routinely given to patients at the check-out desk:
➤ Appointments or appointment confirmations
➤ Prepping instructions for procedures or surgeries
➤ Directions to a laboratory, imaging facility, rehabilitation center,
day surgery, or a referred physician's office
➤ Receipts for payment
➤ Information about referrals, pre-authorizations, and
pre-certifications

Charge entry

One of the most important processes to conclude the patient's visit
is charge entry. Charge entry is necessary for your practice to collect payments. Patient charges must be entered in order to begin
the billing process. The information must be transferred from the
superbill into the practice management system. If this information
is transferred automatically, your job may be to verify accuracy and

completeness; if this information must be keyed into the practice management system, your job may be to enter the data.

Electronic charge entry. Electronic charge entry, available through most electronic health record (EHR) systems, offers the most streamlined process to enter charges. When physicians complete the documentation of the visit, they choose the procedure code(s) that best describes the services provided and documented. The selected codes then interface with the practice management system to become charges that are billed to the patient and/or the patient's insurance company. Although the transfer may be seamless, your supervisor may assign you responsibility to verify the accuracy and completeness of the information.

Paper charge entry. Manual charge entry features paper superbills (also known as encounter forms or charge tickets) on which a physician can record the services performed. These superbills are designed to feature all of the physicians' commonly used procedure codes in a logical, organized format. The tickets may, for example, provide commonly used diagnoses codes on the back of the form and space for the physician to write out unusual services or procedures performed. Your practice probably updates its superbills every year, and may even use multiple superbills. The CPT® codes (authored and managed by the American Medical Association) are used by physicians to code and bill their services. (An electronic system would accomplish this almost automatically.)

Diagnosis codes are used to identify the disease, injury, or other medical condition. Known as the International Classification of Diseases, 9th Edition (ICD-9; to be replaced by a newer system called ICD-10 in 2013), these codes are based on an international system and are widely accepted in the medical community. Insurance companies require that each CPT code be matched and supported by an ICD-9 code.

Charge capture is critical

Regardless of how charges are entered, checks and balances are important to ensure no charges are missed. A charge that is never entered is never billed — and a charge that is never billed is never paid. The process of auditing daily to discover missing charges is a task your practice should perform. Most practice management and EHR systems have "missing charge" reports that can make an electronic match between the appointment schedule and charges billed. Practices that have both systems in place can run these reports daily to identify charges that were accidentally overlooked, as well as to prevent filing incomplete claims with insurance companies or undercharging patients. Many medical practices, however, do not have a fully functioning EHR, or it may not be well integrated with the practice management system, so tracking missing charges may be a manual system even if your practice is automated.

Finding missing charges by hand is a time-consuming but important task. Be sure to discuss when and how this responsibility should be performed with your supervisor. Automation or not, it is important for the check-out staff to try and spot omissions and mistakes that can lead to missing charges.

Follow-up scheduling

Follow-up scheduling is important for the health of patients. The EHR or a paper superbill can be used by the physician to inform you of the need for and timing of follow-up scheduling. Whatever form this tracking takes, there is a place for the physician to indicate the time a patient may be asked to return for another visit (for example, "two weeks," "four months," etc.). At check-out, you can use this information to give the patient a choice of appointment dates and times to return for the follow-up visit. After the date and time are chosen, offer the patient written confirmation of the appointment.

If you use a practice management or an EHR system, this process may go faster. Your system may be able to print out a confirmation and automatically create a notation in the electronic record to show that the patient was indeed given the follow-up appointment information. The record also may be capable of recording who on staff scheduled the appointment and when they did so. Even when using these electronic systems, many check-out staff members find it convenient to continue writing appointment details on appointment confirmation cards.

It might also be possible to submit the appointment details on your practice's Web-based patient portal. If your practice sends e-mail or text messages to patients, you might offer to communicate the appointment information and a confirmation to the patient. As always, any e-mails or text messages to patients should be done carefully and with the patient's permission. Be sure to consider patient privacy when e-mailing or texting as these systems are often not secure enough to guarantee privacy as legally required. Check with your supervisor before communicating with patients via e-mail or text messages.

Your responsibility at the check-out desk is to translate the physician's recommendation for a subsequent visit into an actual appointment. Performing this administrative process in a timely and accurate manner, while it may be routine for you, is vital to the care of the patient.

Orders

At the end of the encounter, the physician may decide to refer the patient to a specialist(s) and/or for an ancillary service(s), such as an MRI, physical therapy, or other services. Depending on the patient's insurance, a referral may also need to be processed. Processing referrals may simply be handing the patient a pre-printed form — or it may include obtaining a one-time authorization from the patient's insurance company that a test, consult, or other service can be made. Ancillary services, such as physical therapy or an MRI, almost always require a written request — often called an "order" — from the referring physician. These administrative processes may vary depending on your practice management and EHR systems, the protocols used by the entities to which you refer patients, and the processes required by the insurance companies.

You may have options as to when and where to perform the required functions of processing a referral. Some practices choose to schedule all recommended care for patients as they wait at check-out; others communicate the information about the recommended care to the patient but perform the scheduling functions at a later time and then communicate with the patient by phone, mail, e-mail, or other means.

Whether scheduling a follow-up visit with one of your physicians or assisting the patient with an appointment elsewhere, it's important to understand how to efficiently and effectively help your patients. Take the opportunity to contact the providers and facilities to which your physicians routinely refer patients to learn about how and whom you should call to schedule appointments; discuss any insurance requirements, to include referrals and authorizations, with your business office; and make sure you identify for your supervisor the tools and resources you need to perform these important responsibilities. Finally, understand how, when, and from whom test results are delivered to patients. Why? Because, when you schedule the appointment for any test, patients will certainly ask you these important questions.

To learn more, or refresh your skills in successful patient scheduling, see Chapter 5, Scheduling.

Payments

The check-out desk is the final opportunity to collect payments from patients. You may have no responsibility for collections at the check-out desk if that process is performed completely as patients arrive.

Some practices, however, assign all or partial responsibility for collections to check-out, particularly if the payment must be calculated based on the services that the physician rendered. Why? If the insurance company with which your practice participates requires patients to pay 20 percent coinsurance for their office visits, for example, the amount is impossible to calculate upon the patient's arrival.

Learn about your responsibility for collections from your supervisor. Discuss how, if applicable, you'll identify the amount the patient owes. Ask for a calculator to assist you, as well as a table of the allowed amounts by the most frequently used CPT codes, by insurance company. If you are collecting coinsurance, or another percentage that must be calculated based on the services rendered, rehearse the process with your supervisor.

Review the tips and procedures for effective time-of-collection techniques in Chapter 6, Time-of-Service Payments. Skills and knowledge learned in this chapter can be put to work at the check-out desk.

Opportune time for a review

Given the importance of this position, take the opportunity to review the check-out area in your practice.

➤ Can you readily identify and understand the physician's orders regarding subsequent visits, requests for imaging or lab tests, and referrals to other providers?

➤ Do you have a system to ensure that you receive every super-bill, even if the patient does not need any further care?

➤ Can you efficiently process the physician's orders while the patient is at the check-out desk?

➤ Do you understand which insurance companies require a referral or authorization and how to process these?

➤ Do you have information for patients, in accordance with the services the physician orders (such as instructions to prepare for a procedure, directions to the imaging facility, confirmation cards for appointments, etc.)?

➤ Are printed materials, such as patient reminders, education, and other information stocked, organized, and ready to distribute as needed?

➤ Do you understand the stocking system and know where to obtain or how to print more copies when needed?

➤ Are printed materials located where you can easily find and reach them without leaving your desk?

➤ Do you have the internal telephone extension of the business office handy so you can summon assistance when a patient asks to delay paying for services or wants to work out a payment plan?

➤ If you are serving as primary or back-up telephone operator, do you have the equipment you need to process telephone calls?

➤ Can you efficiently provide patients with receipts for payment?

➤ Can you quickly access a list of local taxi companies, location of nearest bus stops, and telephone number (or Website) of public transit schedules?

As with the registration function, or even the patient examination processes of your practice's clinical team, an efficient check-out desk needs the right tools and resources available. These tools make the process run smoother and ensure that no important steps are missed. The most important resource of all, of course, is you and your knowledge of the responsibilities assigned to the check-out desk.

Conclusion

At the check-out desk, you have a direct role in each patient's health by making sure their physician's orders, including referrals and follow-up appointments, are handled correctly. Your job includes ensuring that important details are completed on the superbill before the billing process can begin. And, finally, check-out is your practice's last opportunity to collect funds from patients before they walk out the door. Billing patients for amounts that should have been collected while they were still in the office is an unnecessary expense to your practice.

CHAPTER 8 QUIZ

True or False

Circle the correct answer.

1. Check-out doesn't have any relation to telephone operations. T　F

2. Missing charges are always caught by the business office, so they aren't an important responsibility of the check-out staff. T　F

3. Getting insurance approval for procedures or diagnostics ordered by the physician is a function that check-out staff may need to perform. T　F

4. Making sure patients have the information they need at check-out helps reduce the need for patients to call the practice later on. T　F

5. Billing patients for amounts that could have been collected while they were still in the office is an unnecessary expense to your practice. T　F

Multiple Choice

Choose the one correct answer to each question.

1. If your practice has an EHR system that performs the charge entry process automatically, your responsibility may include:
   a. Turning on the computer every time a patient is seen
   b. Verifying the accuracy and completeness of the charges
   c. Changing the diagnosis code
   d. Verifying that a "V-code" is being used for every patient

2. Check-out may include the following responsibility(ies):
   a. Scheduling follow-up appointments at your practice
   b. Scheduling appointments with other physicians
   c. Collecting payments
   d. All of the above

3. Charges may be entered:
   a. Electronically
   b. Manually from paper superbills
   c. Either a or b.
   d. Only by physicians

4. Information routinely given out to patients at the check-out desk includes:
   a. Appointments or appointment confirmations
   b. Instructions to prepare for procedures or surgeries
   c. Directions to a laboratory, imaging facility, rehabilitation center, day surgery center, or a referred physician's office
   d. All of the above

5. Ancillary services, such as physical therapy or MRI, almost always require a physician's written request, often called a/an:
   a. Order
   b. ICD-9
   c. CPT
   d. Charge entry

Matching

Enter the letter of the correct definition from the right column next to the term in the left column that is the best match.

1. __ Superbill, charge   a. Proprietary system for coding
   ticket, encounter   physician services.
   form   b. Classification of diagnoses used for
2. __ CPT   coding physician services.
3. __ Physician orders   c. Identifies services for which
4. __ ICD-9   charges were not entered into the
5. __ Authorization   billing system.
6. __ Missing charge   d. Paper or electronic form to record
   report   physician charges.
7. __ Appointment   e. Referring the patient for a test or to
   confirmation card   another physician.
                            f. Insurance company's approval for a
                               service or test.
                            g. Written appointment reminder given
                               to a patient at check-out.

Answers to this quiz are in Appendix B.

[CHAPTER 9]

Conclusion

As a member of the front office team, your position is vital to your practice. You help the practice to operate efficiently and effectively. Your actions make patients feel that they are treated with respect and have been facilitated in reaching their physicians. In this important role, you may be called upon to perform a host of functions, to include:

➤ Providing customer service;

➤ Receiving patients;

➤ Registering patients;

➤ Answering telephones;

➤ Scheduling appointments;

➤ Collecting payments;

➤ Managing waiting patients; and

➤ Checking out patients.

Your job, however, goes beyond just completing these various tasks and responsibilities. You are one of your practice's key players in pleasing patients and presenting your practice in a favorable light to new patients as well as established ones.

As the first person patients see, you establish the patient's perception about the practice. Eye contact and a smile mean a positive experience. Even if the patient is too ill, weak, or tired to express thanks, they are grateful.

Patients rarely walk out if you fail to display warmth, but rest assured, they remember the experience. Your interactions can make the difference between patients feeling that your medical practice is a harbor of comfort and understanding of their illness — or a cold, stressful, and intimidating place. These reactions may not always be readily apparent, but they are formed in each patient's mind. As the "front-door" to the practice, you are the one who can make — or break — the patient's favorable impression of the entire organization.

In addition to the functions and responsibilities we have described in this book's chapters, you are your practice's:

> ➤ **Director of First Impressions.** You make the difference between a patient who is "wow'd" and one who has a stale, impersonal experience.

> ➤ **Director of New Business Development.** You accommodate patients as they call and present. You schedule appointments that make the best use of your provider's time.

> ➤ **Director of Time-of-Service Finance.** Your role in collecting payments at the time of service means the difference between a successful revenue cycle or an accounts receivable that's old and impossible to fully collect.

> ➤ **Director of Denials Prevention.** Your attention to detail and timeliness can mean your practice is paid accurately. You play a critical role in preventing denials, thus reducing the workload of your colleagues in the business office, and improving the cash flow of your practice.

You are the first and last point of contact for every patient visit. You are the voice of your practice on the telephone. You are vital to your practice — and your patients.

This book seeks to deliver a basic foundation in the key ingredients of successful performance at the front desk. Ultimately, successful performance requires a strong work ethic, thorough knowledge of your practice, technical skills appropriate to your role, and a genuine desire to help patients.

As technology, regulations, and reimbursement evolve, your responsibilities will certainly shift. The key to long-term success, then, is to be a constant student — you can never learn enough. Likewise, there are always opportunities to support the other members of your team and no end to the ways in which you can put the patient first.

Best wishes to you for a successful career in the front office.

Questions for Front Office Supervisors

To examine the implementation and application of the lessons in this book from the supervisor's point of view, consider how you as a supervisor of front office staff would answer these questions. Replies that are answered "no" or "not sure" may be good places to start to improve performance.

❑ Are front office staff aware of what is expected of them?

❑ Do you have a position description for each job title?

❑ Do you have department policies and protocols in writing?

❑ Are front office staff at all clinical sites following the exact same department policies and protocols?

❑ Are front office staff schedules posted weekly, bi-weekly, or monthly?

❑ Who coordinates and approves front office staff leave?

❑ Are front office staff praised for positive performance?

❑ Are front office staff provided routine feedback regarding job performance and proficiency?

❑ Do you have a rewards and recognition program for your front office staff?

❑ Is job performance and proficiency, as well as patient service, monitored for all front office staff members regularly?

❑ Are front office staff roles and responsibilities clearly defined?

❑ Do all front office staff members know who their supervisor is?

❑ Do you have regular front office staff meetings?

❑ Are front office staff lunch breaks paid, unpaid, or a combination?

❑ Are all front office staff members oriented to the practice and their specific roles?

❑ Is there a written document and checklist for orientation?

❑ What is the training program for front office staff by position?

❑ Are front office staff members crossed-trained to other roles within their scope?

❑ Do front office staff members understand how to effectively utilize the practice management system?

❑ Do front office staff members understand how to effectively utilize the telephone system?

❑ Do front office staff members dress professionally?

❑ Do front office staff members wear nametags?

❑ What is the process for avoiding, monitoring, and disciplining front office staff for unplanned absences and lateness?

❑ Do you have a front office staff counseling and disciplinary action process?

❑ Who is responsible for front office staff schedules, to include ensuring coverage for time off?

❑ Are front office staff work hours conducive to office hours?

❑ Do you monitor front office staff overtime? What actions do you take to reduce it?

❑ Does the front office staff treat patients with respect and care at all times?

❑ Do you have a process for recruitment and interviewing?

❑ Are exit interviews conducted with front office staff members who are leaving?

❑ Are front office staff turnover rates monitored?

❑ Are front office staff members satisfied by their work?

❑ Does the front office staff feel committed to your practice and your patients?

❑ Is there a pathway for front office staff to move upward?

❑ Do you encourage front office staff development and continuing education?

❑ Is teamwork in the front office promoted and encouraged?

❑ Are front office staff members provided with all of the tools and resources they need to perform their jobs?

Answer Keys to Self-test Quizzes

Chapter 1
True or False: 1=T; 2=F; 3=T; 4=T; 5=F; 6=T
Multiple Choice: 1=d; 2=b; 3=a; 4=d; 5=b; 6=d
Matching: 1=f; 2=c; 3=d; 4=e; 5=b; 6=a

Chapter 2
True or False: 1=T; 2=F; 3=T; 4=F; 5=T
Multiple Choice: 1=b; 2=d; 3=d; 4=b; 5=a; 6=c
Matching: 1=a; 2=e; 3=b; 4=c; 5=a

Chapter 3
True or False: 1=T; 2=F; 3=T; 4=T; 5=F
Multiple Choice: 1=d; 2=d; 3=a; 4=b; 5=c; 6=d
Matching: 1=e; 2=f; 3=d; 4=b; 5=a; 6=c

Chapter 4
True or False: 1=T; 2=F; 3=T; 4=F; 5=T
Multiple Choice: 1=d; 2=a; 3=d; 4=b; 5=c; 6=c
Matching: 1=d; 2=e; 3=g; 4=f; 5=a; 6=c; 7=b

Chapter 5
True or False: 1=T; 2=T; 3=T; 4=T; 5=F; 6=T; 7=F
Multiple Choice: 1=b; 2=d; 3=b; 4=c; 5=d; 6=d; 7=b
Matching: 1=b; 2=i; 3=a; 4=c; 5=g; 6=e; 7=f; 8=h; 9=j; 10=d

Chapter 6
Multiple Choice: 1=d; 2=a; 3=a; 4=d; 5=b
Matching: 1=d; 2=e; 3=a; 4=b; 5=c
Math Problems: 1=$16.65; 2=$51.87; 3=$582.46; 4=$149.10

Chapter 7
True or False: 1=F; 2=T; 3=T; 4=F; 5=T; 6=F
Multiple Choice: 1=d; 2=d; 3=b; 4=d; 5=d
Matching: 1=d; 2=f; 3=a; 4=c; 5=b; 6=e

Chapter 8
True or False: 1=F; 2=F; 3=T; 4=T; 5=T
Multiple Choice: 1=b; 2=d; 3=c; 4=d; 5=a
Matching: 1=d; 2=a; 3=e; 4=b; 5=f; 6=c; 7=g

Index

About the CD

• •

Included with this book is a CD-ROM containing Quizzes, Answer Key, Questions for Supervisors, Scripts, and other Tools.

How to Use the Files on Your CD-ROM

You must have Microsoft®Word installed on your hard drive to use the CD-ROM. To adapt the files to your own practice, simply follow the instructions below. The CD-ROM will work on Windows and Mac platforms. A list of links to all support files are in the document named "Contents.doc."

Microsoft®Word Instructions for Windows

1. Load the CD in your CD-ROM drive. The file "Contents.doc" will open in Microsoft®Word unless you have autorun disabled. If the file does not open automatically, go to *My Computer* and then the CD drive, and open the file.

2. Control-click a name on the list to open the linked Microsoft®Word file.

Microsoft®Word Instructions for Mac OS X

1. Insert the CD in your CD-ROM drive. A CD icon will appear on your desktop.

2. Click a name on the list to open the linked Microsoft®Word file.

Use the "Save as..." command under the file menu or Office Button to save the file to your hard drive and edit to suit your practice.